$4-T^2D^2$
THE EQUATION

$4-T^2D^2$
THE EQUATION

Yes After Yesterday

YES AFTER YESTERDAY

JAMES TARANTIN

THE EQUATION

This edition first published in 2013.

Copyright 2011 TarantinDream LLC

The Equation, The Galaxy of Gods, names characters, and related indicia are copyright and trademark of TarantinDream LLC

ISBN 978-0-615-75396-6 (Paperback)

Trademark Title - M.P.A.A. ® Title

WWW.THE-EQUATION.COM

CONTENTS

PART THREE

THE DARK DAYS

PART FOUR

THE RETURN OF THE LIGHT

To My Heavenly Mother

&

The World

PROLOGUE

Over 13 billion years ago ...when the universe sparked to *life* ... the spiritual Big Bang accelerated fluctuations of light that swept the void of space with galaxies and *dark* energy.

Within this creation, a promise was made. In its heart lies the greatest light. The watchmaker watched the creation, as the universe was endowed with *the freedom* to move on its own.

One infinite garden, yet many trees of life. One humanity, yet many stories. This book is a small story from the inner light: a story that shall explore the Physical World and the Spiritual World. The body of the story shall embark upon exotic adventures across the lands of Planet Earth: from the continent of Asia to the continent of Europe, and from the ancient civilizations of the Middle East to the continent of America.

The mind of the story will travel from a little roof to the vastness of the stars, from the fires of the valleys to spiritual summits, from War to Peace, and from the sorrows of a heart to the pursuit of a dream.

There is a treasure. Yes! There is a treasure. A treasure that had been lost for millennia, hidden in the margins of History. A force beyond Time and Space – the source of all innovations. The myth tells that whoever discovers this treasure shall be bestowed *4 Rings of Power*: *The Fountain of Youth* – Water, *Designing Destinies* – Wind, *The Moment* – Earth, and *Cosmic Energy* – Fire.

So let us light the torch of the future and sail towards the *unseen*!

PART 1
THE DAWN

CHAPTER 1
The Harmony of Heaven

An exchange of energy always occurs among all living things. Within this circle, within this network of energy … a small family once lived. But in order for the family to be here today, past generations decided to design the *sands of time*.

With no fuel or oil, every day, 7 days a week, Planet Earth orbits the sun. Every dawn, when the morning star shines high above, *a new hope* is born. A long time ago, in a far away holy land, on one of these mornings, an old man named Mati decided to *transform* his lemon into lemonade.

The old man and his wife had lost all their children. And the doctors declared that the wife was now barren, unable to continue their lineage. Living in the palace of poverty, their tent couldn't cover their heads against the rain. But no ceiling could defer their dreams.

Mati, a tall skinny man with wise, white hair, decided to believe … to free his mind and take a leap of faith.

That winter, for 3 days and nights, he traveled to a sacred site. Though dangers lurked in every corner – cloaked strangers, hunger, and fatigue tested the old man along the way – he reached the grave of a great king.

The old man fell to his knees. He closed his eyes and let his lips spill the wishes of his heart, like a spiritual seeker chanting a prayer…

Creator of the universe…
Bestow upon me your compassion…
For I have lost all my children and my pockets are empty
though I iron sick peoples' clothes.
Dust I am I do know, but my heart is wide open.
Gift me one son … bless his future generations
and I shall name him after The King I kneel before today.

A *tear* fell from the old man's eye. Mati walked out the gates of the holy city. As he stood alone on the ancient brick floors, suddenly a bill of currency was delivered by a gentle breeze. The old man grasped the proceeds. He looked to the stars and whispered, "We thank you."

11 months later, which is one drop in the universe's clock, Mati's wife gave birth to a son: David.

Growing up to become a young lad with straight black hair, a constant smile, and a jovial voice that perpetually beamed optimism, David would journey all across the holy land. Lying in the grass under the kisses of the sun, David kindled exotic dreams that would shatter when he saw the social divides tearing the terrain.

David was a young Casanova. Battles with barons of wealth who offered him no opportunities because of his dark skin, the lavish lives of elite Marie Antoinettes… all did nothing to diminish David's delight in everything he saw.

David believed in liberty and the self-reliance bestowed upon man. The poetic lad was somewhere between a military general with his feet on the ground and a pilot with his head in the clouds.

David dreamed that one day, through passion and perspiration, his future family would be able to sit in the seats of status, a place which he presently could not be.

After exploring Europe – experiencing the English Channel, the peaceful fields of Switzerland, the aroma of the Italian coffee, and the seas of Sweden – at the age of 24, the young man decided to take destiny into his own hands; he launched … a street cleaning enterprise.

Climbing the mountain towards accomplishment, he always remembered to descend and lift others up. Driving during the summer's heat, David would get out of the truck to give a hand to the white bearded men lifting trash from the street.

Every person, today or in the past, has kept little trophies that inspire the mind to nostalgically recall the days when one was *forever young.*

David's trophy, his Casanova-like badge, was a little black book with the numbers of over 1,200 women. And by the age of 29, his manly friends vehemently verified this legend.

There is a myth.
Thousands of years ago, in *Egypt* … the Pharaoh suspected that a little boy, delivered by the waters to his empire, would one day

become a danger. So the mighty Pharaoh put the boy to the test. He assembled the entire royal household and arranged them in a circle. The boy was placed in the center with a stack of gold and burning stones. The Pharaoh declared: "If the boy shall touch the gold, I shall smite him for he is of a *dark danger*. Alas! Here I say unto you, if the boy shall *decide* to touch the stones, he shall *transform* into … the Prince of Egypt."

The crowd stood frozen as the Egyptian king cast critical eyes at the alienated boy, who began to crawl ahead. The gold shone against the boy's eyes, alluring his delicate finger to touch its sparkling solemn light. When the Pharaoh unsheathed his sword and held it up, prepared to strike, suddenly an invisible *angel passed by* and touched the hand of the boy. *The tragedy* left the boy scarred … only to *transform* him into The Prince and later free the slaves, who were like gold for the Egyptian king.

One morning … David decided to take the same habitual route to work. His enterprise was self-enriching due to David's self-reliance. As David was about to turn the wheel towards the way he knew, without warning, yet exactly on time, an *angel passed by* and jarred the wheel to a new path.

As the dust of the earth rolled in the air, David's star shone on the horizon; a lady in pure white strolled by. And instead of collecting a new number in the black book, he *decided* to lay it to rest.

David's charisma and panache were awakened. The lady remained reserved. And David said, "I would be honored if you would join me at a gala I am conducting on Friday."

A few days elapsed. Then a call. "Hello?" David answered. "Hi David, this is Miriam. I would like to accompany you this Friday. But I can't stay late. My curfew is 11 PM. Where do you live?"

The young couple marveled at the currents of destiny when they discovered that only 4 streets separated them. David picked Miriam up, and love was soaring with the birds.

Wishes Come True

After passing the test of time, during one bright night, David decided to hold Miriam's hand and ride with her to an apartment in

4

an upper-class city. On the way, David disclosed to his Cleopatra that he would appreciate her advice on an apartment he was contemplating purchasing.

When the doorknob turned, the young lady's heart fell silent. Consumed by his excitement, David hurried to the kitchen. "Miriam you have to see this…" Scouting around, David discovered that his loved one was gone.

The white silk drape was waving in the wind, revealing the little lady standing on the terrace, viewing the stars of the night.

David cautiously walked to her kingdom and whispered: "Are you all right my love?"

As an orphan girl who once dared to dream for a teddy bear, Miriam replied, "I can't believe I am in this place, David. I had no home when I was growing up. My dorm was tiny with old cement floors and small windows overlooking the cows I had to milk every dawn. I wished for a little home of my own. And now… 23 years later, you bring me here. I ask myself if it's a dream or reality?"

A tender wind began to blow as David kneeled under the stars and said, "My darling! This home is yours. I acquired it for you."

Tears of joy rained from the homeless girl's eyes. David asked, "My love … will you marry me?" And a celestial kiss sealed their union.

∞

A year later… the freshly married lady felt her first labor pains and gave birth to her son: Omer.

That was my name … that was my name …

∞

As a family, we were as close to one another as the branches that sprout from the tree of life; as a band of birds flying with the synergy of a flock. Laughing, sharing, holding hands, kissing and hugging were our Manna and Elixir.

The family's belief in higher powers was a dove that would land every morning in our home to deliver hope.

My mother would wake up and say, "What is the meaning of *value*? … pure value?" And she would put her motherly hand against her heart and say, "Pure value happens before the separation, before the division. There was a time when left and right were *one*.

5

When black and white were one. When the 4 elements were one. When the spiritual and the physical were one."

She coined a phrase …

An ancient heart and an innovative mind

"Each human being is a divine canvas. We are the painters of the picture. No matter how great the will is to innovate and expand the painting, the mind, one should balance the painting with a traditional frame, the heart."

My mother says that by the age of 14 months I was barely dragging myself along the floor of the house. Only the love for animation running across the screen could motivate my muscles.

So one afternoon, Miriam put the remote on a little table and said, "If you want to pursue your love, stand up."

For a long time, her soul was *pained* as she heard her son shed *tears*. Then, the sounds were suspended. Peeking from the kitchen, she saw a little boy struggling to stand up by holding one of the table's *columns*.

The boy saw a *star*, a book next to the remote. He grasped it and crawled back to his mother. Tears flowed from her eyes when she opened the book and its first page read: "*Let There Be Light.*"

Growing up, I loved and respected my father. I hoped to one day be as good and as kind to my future generations as he was to me.

Nevertheless, the love I felt for my father was but a drop in the ocean compared to the love I had for my mother.

My mother! Oh! My mother. I was fascinated by her like a fawn that follows his doe as a guiding star. She was a pianist, a poet, a painter, and a spiritual mentor. If I have ever seen farther, or evolved my mind higher, it is because she wrapped my spirit with love and lullabies. No matter how far my odyssey did sail, I always praised her enormously, declaring that she was an archangel in disguise.

I was a lively boy, sprinting across the house, alert with kinetic eagerness. To diffuse the waves of energy, my mother would let me watch *The Ten Commandments*. My eyes would grow wide open, giving Miriam the time to deal with the domestic duties.

Children are young explorers inspired to discover a world *free* from blocks and barriers, and their eyes are fairy-tale like telescopes.

There was a song my father revered: "Forsake Us Not At Our Old Age." Whenever the musical notes resonated in his ears, a lonely *tear* would run down his cheek.

These *tears* unlocked a door in my *child mind*, and I developed a deep connection and compassion for the poor and elderly. I felt my existence was intertwined with theirs. There were blissful days when I would run to the old neighbors and offer them assistance with their baskets. They would ask, "Son, don't you want to play with other children and have fun?" And I would reply, "I believe that this is my fun." Or when my father couldn't find his wine bottles, he would find a defiant glare upon his complaint, "It is a very expensive habit to give to strangers every day."

The Kinship among all living things.
I *remember* my first day in kindergarten. On the way, my mother said, "My light, today you are about to officially begin your life…are you excited?" My sour face refused to respond.
When my mother and I arrived, I saw such an abundance of celestial children that I believed they could breathe life into a forest. I was afraid yet curious, hiding behind my mother's legs. While all the kids were playing in paradise, a wizardly kindergarten teacher came forth to welcome me. "Who is the boy?" she gently asked. With a hesitant hide-and-seek expression on my face, I was shyly alert.

My mother lowered her palm, caressed my cheek and said, "Aren't you going to introduce yourself?"

Looking to my mother I pushed out my lower lip, furrowed my eyebrows, and stayed silent. The teacher came down until her eyes were level with mine, and her tender voice traveled in the air, "I am not going to bite. Here, I want to give you this flower." Glancing at my mother for a blessing, I touched and then *picked up* the flower. "My name is Omer" I said.

"Nice to meet you," my teacher replied. "Do you want to walk with me to the garden?" We exchanged glances, and my teacher flowed with *the moment*. Noticing my reluctance, she smiled at my mother and said, "Alright, we will wait for you …" and then floated through the gate.

"My light," my mother said tenderly … "It's time for you to begin your life … all the children are already inside." I felt the clouds were dividing the kingdom of the skies, and a breeze of solitude blew against my skin. Bursting into *tears*, I replied: "I so *afraid* mama … I don't want to go there …"

My mother reached out her arms and embraced my little body. "Don't be afraid my light," she whispered. "Will I ever see you again?" I whimpered.

The mother raised her 2 fingers and gently lifted her son's chin. "Oh! My darling, I will always be right here." Our hands met in mid-air.

"Now, I want you to be brave and open the gate." She cleared away the tears that painted my face. She kissed me on the forehead, and I was headed towards the sounds of heaven.

The currents of the moment carried me across the garden, and I slipped into the kindergarten's chamber. The children were sitting in a circle on wooden chairs. They were all holding toy torches that displayed a little painting of children holding hands, crowned by a rainbow.

"Good morning!" the wizardly teacher greeted the class. "My name is Raquel, and I am your teacher."

One of the children naively asked, "What are these things we're holding?" The enchanting voice of the teacher echoed, "These are torches of *Light*. Each one of you is a color in the rainbow, a unique angel … and together, *we light*!"

A little princess with golden curls lit up at these words, and full of awe, declared, "Hi! … my mother told me about the angels." She stood up and announced, "*I want to be an Angel,*" lifting the torch triumphantly.

Right then, one by one, the children of Earth stood up and proclaimed,

"I WANT TO BE AN ANGEL!"

CHAPTER 2
The Eagle Holds The Spear of War and The Language of Peace.

The clock of the universe continued to tick, and I became 5 years old. After years of watching animations surging on the screen, I began to *pick up* and build a certain *second nature* attachment to the English language.

My mother *decided* to send me to the estates of private tutors all across the holy land. The tutors' cultural colors ranged across a rich palate: British, American, Australian, and Irish.

With them, I learned the text. But only with my mother did I pick up the *subtext*. With her *broken* accent she would impart the dynamics of English, noting the tempo changes between flat realism and poetry. Her wand-like finger would point to her lips, which produced the sounds like a magical piano, lighting the path to absorb the words emotionally.

As life's clock ticked forward, I would lament that although I dreamt in English, my mouth manufactured sounds that were unconventional. My motherly guardian would reply,
"A disadvantage today is the advantage of tomorrow. Discover the unity in the variety of your higher self."

It was a beautiful afternoon when my mother and I were strolling back home. As she turned the knob, the door resembled a silk handkerchief carrying with it noises from the underworld.

The living room *darkened*. My mother's face went pale. And I watched the screen delivering English lyrics my mind couldn't interpret. A sparkle of history flashed in my eyes, and I remembered what the teacher had said that very day: "Children, we might not see one another for quite some time. Be good and trust *mankind*".

"What happened, Mama?" the curious mind of a child craved to know. Staring at the screen, she said, "*Jerusalem is at War*"

The American eagle held its spear and set Operation Desert Storm in motion. The allies on the other side of the world transported their children to a special shelter built of strong bricks and cement.

Scud missiles from Baghdad were launched on the holy land. *The war siren* screamed across the skies as though a *dark* Greek goddess was shattering the afterlife in inferno.

Gas masks resembled Roman helmets; my brother held captive in a shielded cage; the cries of tormented souls brought a smile to the boatman … all came to attack and tremble the *cosmic clock*.

I bolted upright, surrounded by a bundle of blankets, as all of a sudden the electricity fell dead. My father said to his wife, "Care for the kids; I'll go to check on the neighbors." He stood up. I followed him. And with a quivering voice, I asked: "Dad, will you be back? The *darkness* scares me."

"I will be back son." He spoke with a sense of assurance. He looked at me and disappeared into *the shades of the night*.

Centuries ago, Baghdad was a city of enlightenment, while other parts of the planet were shrouded in the dark ages. Now its lands were on fire.

My mother would watch the horrors of war on the screen and say, "If a human being dies anywhere in the world, a piece of me dies too."

As all living things are interconnected … so are the body and the mind. One midnight, the alarm clock of my body sounded its siren: my left leg became numb. The freedom of walking on 2 legs was ruptured.

My father held me in his arms. With a roar, the engine woke to life and off we drove to the emergency room. The streets were deserted like a desolate dream, as a ferocious storm poured *TEARS* from the kingdom of the clouds'.

On our way back home, reality seemed to *transform*. Back to square one, my mother said, "*Armageddon* is over. But its theme is still alive."

10

CHAPTER 3
The Reflection of The Water

One afternoon, my mother and I were ambling along together, eating ice cream. When we reached the top of our stairs, a cone crashed against the floor as my mother saw that our house's door was slightly open.

"Stay here," she whispered.

Alone in the *lightless* aisle, I lost a sense of *time,* and *decided* to go in. My home had been seized and thrown into an abyss. Many objects were gone, and my mother was sitting in the center of the living room, reading a letter. "Go to your room," my mother said. "Is everything all right, Mother?" I asked helplessly. "Go to your room, my light." Miriam remained collected.

The walls confining my room proved to be too thin to soundproof my mother's voice as she rang my father and told bits of the tale …

… The Collateral Connection …
… Secret Provision …
… Trusted him …
… Loophole …

Later that night, my father came home. He bellowed, "That bastard, I should…"

"You are your own judge," my mother stated firmly. "Bad decisions lured you to follow the man's charm and knowledge." A ray of hope emanated from David: "The *future* of our family hangs by a thread … what happens if we *fail*?"

Miriam revealed her composure. "Henry Ford went broke before he transformed the world."

"So what should we do?" *Logic* asked *Intuition*. "*Transform*. Evolve higher … because you are … in a low valley."

Lying in my tiny bed beneath the blanket, I saw a fairy float into my room as a *nightlight*. My mother whispered, "My little Moses." She kissed me on the forehead, and I asked, "Will everything be alright mother?" Caressing my cheek, she started to sing a little lullaby, and I entered the Neverland of *dreams*.

7 days later, the fruits of my father's labor were saved. But more important are the lessons ... a child *picks up*.

The Last Moment

The mental state and the actions of a human being in the face of a crisis ...
those little moments of *Death*, purely reveal the character.
Life repeats itself. Years pass by, and one blindly believes that the face of a friend is known.
Fun, charm, knowledge, and experience camouflage the subtext.
Yet *tragedies* do what time won't.

There Is No Time

The watch on the wrist is an illusion. The dimension of time exists for the mind, which chases what doesn't matter – the bystander.
Time causes the mind to be in a prison of patterns.
True game-changers, the architects of the future ...
Never follow time.
... *Time follows them* ...

When a new Solar System is sparked to life (an Innovation)... Does the Universe ask what time it is?

David endured ... and now decided to undertake a new enterprise: flags and *symbols*. My mother says that he was a master seller and that his sense of humor could sell ice to Antarctica.

David never believed in connections ... he believed in *friends*. Though he came from the commoner's class, our home would host celebrations and banquets serving social *ambrosia*. 5-star generals, chief ministers, supreme judges, and honorees ... all would be superseded the next day, when he would drink coffee with a poor street cleaner.

David sacrificed precious moments with his family. Traveling to distant places paying homage to friends, gatherings when the *clock stopped*, and working late hours along with the orbits of the moon, all brought a measure of serenity to *The Way to Wealth*.

But this *luck* ... was a double-edged sword for a dark-skinned boy.

The throne of liberty was cast to the gutter as the clashes between the commoners and aristocrats carried on for over 100 years. Deferred dreams, despair, and *tears* encapsulated my cradle. Yet often times, the mind of a child ... is not aware.

The boy was very excited. 7 days before his first day at the next school, his mother bought clothes for him, and he played carefree games under the skies ... not knowing that his skin color had a bond with the sun.

The next day, 3 buses came to pick up the children. The white students gave dirty looks to a dark-skinned kid. Danger crept from hidden corners, but the child's hope blazed in his eyes like a landscape with cascading waterfall.

The buses reached their destination. The children happily ran to the pool. From the back of the bus ... the child walked forward to join them.

The sun burned in the skies, and only the whistling wind could be heard. With fear, the child took off his shirt and entered the pool in his swim suit.

Time Stopped. The white students leapt to their feet. The dark color of the commoner child reflected against the waters.

A bewildered stare crept upon the child's face as the other children ... departed from the pool.

And that day ... would fill the pages of the past with a scarring echo ...

Black in the back ... black in the back ...

Parallel years were lost.

One afternoon, living nature flooded into my heart as I walked with my mother, holding her hand. A little chocolate bar peeked from my pocket, enticing my senses. As my hand reached for it, a voice induced a vertigo of values.

"What are you doing?" my mother demanded. "Just eating my chocolate bar, mother," I quietly replied. "Be mindful of your *decisions,* son. Can you see this poor man sitting in the lonely corner?" she inquired, pointing to the feeble figure. "Yeah, I can see him," I said. "Do your *eyes* see him … or your *heart*?"

"Umm…I…"

"Let your inner light guide you; don't fall into your senses. This old man would give a lot for this chocolate bar you take for granted."

"What should I do, mother?" I looked up to her as to reset my compass. "This is your *freedom,* my light. Your *Decision.* I can only show the door, but *you* have to walk through it."

The sweet scent of the chocolate bar accelerated an adrenaline rush, but looking over at the poor man, my heart seeped in sadness.

I approached the man and said, "'Scuse me sir, may I give you my chocolate bar? My mother bought it for me, and I want you to have it." The man's eyes lit up, as though no living thing had ever spoken to him. He reached for the bar … and a better adrenaline rush ran through my heart.

The earth shook a bit when my mother and I arrived at the building's gate. A gang of 6 from the aristocratic class were chanting chilling hymns. My mother said, "Come on son, let's take the other way." But their eyes caught us. Like tigers on the move, they gazed and sounded minor roars.

Suddenly life started to move in *slow motion.* It seemed like the walls of space were bending. I walked forward. The white gang started to laugh at my height. Then it seemed as though *a clock stopped ticking.* The gang fled … and a mother and her child could pass.

CHAPTER 4
The Louvre Voyage

As my formal education on this planet continued, my mother embraced the belief that no palace or parliament is a better school than the living world.

The first new world I would visit was the poetic land of France. 4 days before the voyage, my mentor-like mother sailed my mind to History. The moonlight bathed the room, and illuminated the European map laid out on the table. And the voice of the past would echo

> ... *Tragedy ... Black Plague ... The Roman Empire ...*
> *... The English Channel... War ...*
> *... The City of Lights ...*

My jaw dropped in awe at the sight of the plane. The runway shimmered in a fluorescent glow, the landing lights flashed red, and the thunders of the engines propelled a young boy to ask every minute : "Are we there yet?!"

We stayed at some friends' euro décor apartment. Subsequent questions were answered with a *secret mission* that brought us to Paris's metro. The train – a kaleidoscope of speed and style – carried us to Champs Elyees, where, eating a crispy croissant, I became bored and urged, "Let's go! Let's go ... there are lost treasures!"

After passing through The Arch of Triumph, I became puzzled. Putting the pieces together, I said, "Mother, if there is a thread between General Lafayette and George Washington, there must also be a thread between Paris and Washington D.C., right?" My mother replied, "Well what would that be, I wonder?"

Suddenly the Eiffel Tower appeared on the horizon, and the link was clear. As I craned my neck to see the Eiffel's pinnacle, I observed, "The Iron Lady and the Washington Monument are the tallest obelisks in their cities..." Miriam smiled ...

Ascending the majestic heights of the Eiffel Tower in the iron lift, my eyes took in a panoramic view of Paris, a picture of grandeur. Without turning back, I ran to the railings at the edge of the deck and shouted with happiness:
"TO THE STARS! TO THE STARS!"
My father pulled my arm and thundered, "Shhh! Why are you

shouting?! People are staring." Looking over at my mother, David said, "Your child is getting wild…"

The morning broke with the sound of birds and the scent of freshly baked bread. Those cracks in the loaf, the bakers' *failures,* seemed like *triumph.*

The magical melody of "La Boheme" orchestrated reality in the Atlantis of artists: Montmarte.

With my spirits soaring as I wandered among the poor aspiring painters and singers, a little fight broke out at a nearby restaurant.

David had retrieved a lighter from his pocket, held it in the air, and clicked a kindle to light his cigarette. The smoke cloaked the ambience, causing Miriam to say, "You look like a train of Nicotine." David replied, "Well, I feel wonderful… nothing will stop me from the rush of smoking".

My mother lightly smiled and said, "As you wish…"

Sitting on the side-walk, fascinated by a poor man singing, suddenly I heard a fairy call out: "Omer…Omer…."

Half somber, half wishful, I walked to my mother. "My light," she said. "Would you want to gift this money to the poor singer?"

My heart leapt. "Yes!" I replied. "Good … when you are done, I will give you more." I ran to the poor singer. I gave him the money. I ran back to my mother. She gave me another bill. I sprinted to a violinist. Back and forth, back and forth … until my father shouted, "Enough! Alright, I will stop smoking." Sitting on the chair, my mother embraced her arriving son. I raised a fist and declared, "We will fight!"

Right then, the restaurant was screening a classic called Casablanca. Hypnotized, I followed the sounds. *A lonely tear* fell from my eye as I heard La Marianne heroically chant La Marseillaise with an inspiring crowd. *Darkness* had lost and a voice cried, "Viva La France!" mirroring the painting on the wall of *Liberty Leading the People*.

After we dined with the eternal elegance of Gallerie Lafayette, where my father showered his wife with gifts and fragrances, the last station of the voyage was the *Louvre*.

David *decided* not to go along, declaring, "What is this business of painting? People putting secrets in colors. If they want to convey a message, tell them to cut to the chase."

The Louvre's palace was a continuum of secrets.
In the courtyard I saw the futuristic inverted Pyramid that seemed to be composed of little mystical lenses.
As I walked toward it, reaching out my hand, I felt the bells of Notre Dame ringing in the distance, and my mother was inspired to whisper, *"The source of light* is everywhere, my son."

 With a map and a compass we searched and wandered the mazes of the Louvre. We saw archives of lost treasures:

A painting of a Young Beggar – the poverty yet the harmony.
A painting of The Astronomer – the alchemy of the stars.
And the painting of Alexander the Great in Babylon
holding a glorious golden scepter.

 The labyrinth tunneled us ahead. I lost sight of my mother and entered a chamber. There I saw a large-scale painting that ran a chill down my spine. As I stood there transfixed, my mother approached and tousled my black hair. "What is that, mother?" I asked. "This is Jesus driving out the *darkness* from the temple with a whip," my mother replied. "Wow … I also want to drive out the darkness, mother," I naively said. "Spiritual heroism and physical heroism should always be as one. Fight for the light, my love." She hugged me, and my eyes were transfixed on the painting.

The Cures of Magic

Later that summer, my mother traveled to the Kingdom of Belgium to explore their folklore. And the lonely island of school continued …

One break, the boy was ambling along the school's paths. Suddenly a student from the aristocratic class spotted him. "Hey, I thought I told you not to be here, blackie!" he yelled. As the boy lowered his head and walked to the other side, the privileged student pulled a hidden hose beneath the boy's feet. The lad tripped and fell to the ground, slamming into an iron sprinkler, leaving his belly oozing blood all across the lawn.

… I opened my eyes later that night to see that I was in my room intoxicated with medicine. Sounds of my father on the phone were muffled, as they endeavored to reach my ears. "You are imagining; nothing happened."

The doorknob was turned, and David entered the room. I asked: "Where is mother?"

Not listening to logic, the next night, my mother returned from Belgium to her child.

$$\infty$$

On the terrace, my mother and I sat facing one another, while colorful beams of orange and red showered fairy dust before dusk.

"My light," my mother sighed. "I want to guide you in how to heal yourself."

Connecting to the mysterious and intangible strata of the soul, she straightened her spine like a spiritual seeker and sunk into a transcendental meditation. My mouth opened like a gaping fish, as she said, "Be a *Knight of Light*. Live with chivalry by letting your inner light shine through you. Unite with all living things. Remember that each human is an unlimited being".

I closed my eyes and aspired to sink into the sensation of seizing the moment. My mother then whispered, "Bend your mind, and the universe will bend with you. Imagine bubbles of energy flowing through your body … like the ones you play with in the bathtub. Set them on fire, for heat heals as much as water does." The wind was blowing as though it was dedicating itself to all the girls it had loved before. I tried to focus on my core.

"Don't try. *Free your mind* … transform into your higher self." My guide paved the way. "What is the higher self, mother?"

"It is a super character you create within you to achieve your dreams." She closed her eyes, focused the laser of her third eye, and then reached her palm to my wound. Feeling the curing heat being transferred into my tissues, Miriam leaned back, opened her eyes, and said, "Your turn."

Quite perplexed, I closed my eyes. Slowly I started to feel flushes of heat spiraling up the passages of my body. Little vibrations shook my hand. I reached it forward. My mother wrapped my hand with her 2 palms. The sun was nearly set … and my mother said, "I am proud of you, son."

18

CHAPTER 5
A Shooting Star

One day after school, the students gathered together to go and play. My longing to join them met with opposition. The day before, my mother had requested that I pick up my brother from Kindergarten, walk him to an unknown address, and not return home.

The next day, street after street was met with a *dead end*. My brother held my hand; our hope seemed lost. Then, at the *last moment*, just as I thought our parents had left us alone in the jungle of life, an angelic voice cried from the heavens, "My children!"

I looked up; on a utopian terrace, my mother waved. Running down the marble stairs, she hugged her children. "This is our new home, my loves." An epic white structure with Trojan walls and an asphalt courtyard, hooked my heart. "What do you say? Shall we go inside?" Miriam asked. She lifted my brother in the air blithely, and a tender wind began to blow, leaving a gap between us as they skipped to the gate.

Following a whirling leaf, I turned away and meandered to a cluster of little sandy hills arranged in a line. Climbing up on the ancient sand, I came upon a borderless green field. And it seemed that the tiny grass blades were singing *Time's Silent Secret*. That night, I was lying in my new blue bed and touching the ceiling that vaulted the stories of the castle. Shafts of soothing moonlight sneaked into my loft through the window. This sense of change led me out of my room to discover a hidden door. I rotated the knob of the door, and under the starry skies I found a private sanctuary: a romantic roof from which it seemed I could see the galaxy.

Its titanic size shattered the dimension of time. And for the rest of my lonely youth, every night, I would escape to the breathtaking beauty of billions of stars casting a milky illumination over the green field.

That first night ... the coolness and crispness of the air against my skin and a *shooting star* that resembled a *heavenly tear* propelled me to step up on the railings and shout to the skies, "I love the world!"

Then, melodious sounds ascended to the roof; the piano was playing ... I scurried back to the house, hurried down the stairs, hid behind the parlor's wall, and glanced at my mother's hands as she sang: "Qué será, será, *whatever will be, will be* ..."

A motherly smile exposed my hiding harbor. And together we danced … in the castle's hall.

CHAPTER 6
The Shangri-La of Enlightenment

A diary reads ... that one wondrous afternoon, on a magical roof, an angelic mother was folding the family's laundry. Her son bent his body as though bearing a burden on his back, placing his folded arms on the railing that overlooked *the green field*.

"Hi, mother," the young boy pointed. "There is a new cleaning man on the street."

"So go and give him fruit and water as you always do when you come home from school."

Solemnly sighing, the boy inquired, "Mother ... why do humans live?" And the mystique of motherhood replied, "For *the dream* of a more hopeful world. A world where all living things are bound together in harmony, like the stars of our galaxy."
She continued:

> *This aspiration knows no distance ...*
> *It has no flag nor hymn ... It*
> *belongs to the spirit of*
> *every human*
> *heart."*

Lifting 2 bags, the mother met her son. "Now I want you to take these 2 bags, and put them under that tree."
"Why can't I give these clothes to the poor cleaning man myself?" the son searched for the answer. "Well, sometimes a man can get embarrassed. When you pass on your compassion silently, its ripples shall reach far." The young lad carried the burden on his back and ran to the tree. He hid behind a nearby hill and hoped the gift would be picked up. Suddenly a little girl swung by. Unwrapping *the present*, she cried, "Grandpa! Grandpa! Look, my prayers came true! The Light sent us these clothes." And while the little angel began to dance, the dark-skinned lad dropped a *tear*.

That twilight, I decided to stand on my roof with a pen and a parchment. I saw the owls' eyes glint like precious stones as they swooped through the trees. Without warning, my eyes caught a group of leaves flying in the air in a circular motion. Subconsciously I noted:

Nothing is new under the sun; made out of dust is one.

Looking more deeply, I picked up a flower, and in the kingdom of the sky, I saw a ballet of birds flying in perfect synergy. Then I revised …

No … dust is done … one is energy.

Consumed by *the moment*, with my legs speeding like a broomstick, I scurried to the house's book collection. My mind echoed one of my mother's sayings: "The biggest empire is the home with the most enlightened library."

Not knowing what I was looking for, books were opened and closed, seemingly whispering, "When science and spirituality are one, confusion shall be washed away."

Unexpectedly, the spine of a book stood out. I picked it up and ran to my mother. Cooking a Latin cuisine, she looked like an Egyptian queen wearing a scarf and a simple dress.
"Mother! … I found this book about cloning; can I have a twin brother?"

Passing by, David said, "One more like you and I migrate to Mars." Steam spiraled from the pots and pans and a mother kept her back to her son. "Decoding the secrets of DNA can cure diseases. Yet cloning is a stock market of human lives – a distorted science," she uttered firmly. "Whether a force is of light or of evil depends upon your perception. And don't forget what the discoverer of $E=MC^2$ said:

As the circle of knowledge expands … so does the circle of Darkness.

Deep in the bowels of the bank of the underworld, a green goblin hobbled along, saying:

The funny joke about conglomerates …
is that the branch can reach record highs…
while the parent tree can reaches record lows.

"And sometimes," the goblin grinned as he faded into the darkness, "The joke is *mirrored*."

While a father reached record highs of golden coins, his son reached a record of lows, as he endured profound loneliness at school.

A new venture in the lands of Asia called upon my father. After his Casanova ways failed to charm his Cleopatra that they should travel alone, the whole household set their eyes on the heart of South Asia.

The Kingdom of Thailand

A map of the world lay unfurled by the bed. "According to the myth," my mother murmured as a bed-time story, "Thailand is the land of the free. It has monarchy with a ruling king, and its calendar is 543 days ahead of the West."

"Ages ago, the Awakened One," she continued as I peered out from under the blanket, "Prince Siddartha ... ignited a dream that changed the continent of Asia forever."

"Wow ... how did he do that, Mother?"
"The Prince was born to a royal family, and the young lad had 2 destinies. The first was to conquer and rule the world, and the second was dependent on his decision to *transform* and endow others with enlightenment."

Soon the airplane, a magical stallion, crossed the seas and lands. The stars of the galaxy drew closer. Then my mother's voice crooned that Bangkok is near. Her eyes spoke volumes when she said that our lodge's name was Shangri-La. A place of utopia, paradise ...

Unlocking the seat-belt, I asked, "Will we see The Source of Light, Mother?!"
My mother caressed my face, her hands like 2 waterfalls and said, "The Source of Light is both invisible and ever-present. It is nowhere ... yet everywhere. Like light and air, we feel it; it permeates the planet."

"But I want to see the light, now!" I stomped my feet. "The universe has its own cosmic clock, quite different from the illusion on your wrist. But sometimes, when people shed *tears* ... their dreams will write the times."

Shangri-La was a palace!

As we neared our chamber, my father warned, "It's pretty small, so measure your movements." Nevertheless, when the door opened, I imagined that a new world wonder was just discovered. The gold, the Asian grandeur, and the views were brilliantly breathtaking. The chamber's space inspired my spirit to search for dragons and ride to the moon on their pearled skin.

As Casanova was engaged in styling his wife in the finest boutiques, the rising red sun of the East made me wish I had 10 more eyes so that I could look in all directions at once.

The ancient Asian bow, a traditional code of honor, greeted me at every turn, and the ripple effect caused me to do the same.

A native long-tail boat sailed us down one of the rivers of Bangkok between banks rich with green forests and rare wildlife. In the sky … a *black* kite flew in circles, searching for prey.

Another boat bumped up alongside ours, my kneels buckled, and a stranger smoking a long pipe proclaimed, "Hello friends, buying something for children, are ya?"

The man's boat was a bazaar of toys. While both boats floated on the river's currents … I fished out a Robin Hood action figure.

My father offered the merchant strange-looking silver coins, and the man handed over … the *archetype* toy.

The long-tail boat docked in a nearby village.

A ring at the center of an arena attracted masses to fix their eyes on a snake show. Cobras and Black Mambas slithered on the floor of the ring and furiously ejected poisonous potion.

Suddenly, the crowd cheered and raised their little glasses of sherry as a gang entered with an exotic emblem sewn on their black jackets. "Who are these people?" a spellbound child asked his mother. "Well, the native folklore tells us that they are a band that steals from the rich and gives to the poor."

"May we join them, Mother?" A child pleaded to play. Miriam replied, "Wrong decisions for good, end up becoming *evil's prey*."

That *night*, in Shangri-La, I had a tough time drifting to sleep. As I gazed at the silent view, my mother floated over to kiss me on the forehead.

"Are you alright, my light?" I spoke silence. "Are you still thinking about the day?" she asked.

"Don't worry, figments of thoughts come and go. Sleep in peace my light … all is bright." She combed my hair, and the chamber ... fell into *darkness*.

On the last day, the Lotus flowers bloomed at a city-like temple in Bangkok. Indigenous monks and kung fu warriors flooded the courtyard, and while these legends meditated and drilled dragon fists, we entered the temple.

At the temple's heart was a gigantic golden statue of the Awakened One, sitting with legs crossed, spine straight, and with thumbs and forefingers joined – resting on each knee.

"Look at these people," David scoffed. "They bow before statues."

"Father, this statue is a symbol of Prince Siddartha." I challenged. "Is it bad to bond with others?" A storm brewed in David's eyes …

"No son of mine shall bow before a statue! I am the breadwinner of the house … and you will obey my command."

At the edge of our time there, while David was away, I looked to my mother. She winked, and I invaded the forbidden temple. The lights illuminating the marble and emeralds guided my third eye, and I followed the path to the altar. The golden statue seemed alive and I said, "Mr. Siddartha … Please forgive my father if he offended you. He is a good man with a lot of humor. Sometimes he makes me laugh so hard my ribs break. I want you to know that I tucked your story under my pillow. I dream that one night a white dragon will fly to all the lonely children and turn their *tears* into *stars*. You were once a child… and tears rained from your eyes too."

Heading back toward the Holy Land, 18 days before my 10th birthday, the Asian adventure stopped in Hong Kong. Its skyline was the meeting place of East and West. The oriental food was foreign to my digestive system, while the British style was featured throughout the colony.

"One country, 2 systems …" Hong Kong would *write its future* 2 years later.

The Asian adventure ended. And the airplane, the magical stallion, crossed the continent and carried a lad to his roof … where he marveled at *The Avenue of the Stars*.

CHAPTER 7
The Basketball of Myths

The luckiest athlete ... is the one ... who wasn't born "talented".

Since I was born, *sparks of talent* had attracted my muscles to athletic tournaments. An *alluring* agility could juggle, run fast, and shot put a ball far distances.

My school was conducting tryouts for the basketball team. For a dark- skinned lad, this chance was like a flying golden unicorn, forecasting the hope of finally finding a friend.

Although I had belligerently bargained with the coach to open the gates for girls to play too, to my surprise the fight didn't deny my inclusion.

Months passed and our team proved to be a contender as we reached the finals.

The arena shook to the sounds of hundreds of students cheering the 2 rival teams, each tagged with its own emblem. The players were warming up on opposite sides of the coliseum-like arena when the announcer shouted from his lofty megaphone, "Ladies aaaaaand Gentlemen! It's our annual celebration. I present to you the best basketball teams that will combat for the trophy." The crowd shot confetti into the air ...

"Are you ready for entertainment?!" The announcer's voice reverberated. "Yeah!" the crowd shouted. "I think my hearing is hindered. Again ... Are you ready for *ENTERTAINMENT*?!"

"YEAH ...!" The players surged to the center of the court. The whistle blew, the ball kissed the zenith of its ascent ... and its fall started the battle.

The players sprang forward. Passes, moves, jumps, and short sprints escalated the teams' scores. An opponent tried to pass the ball to his mate; I leapt up, intercepted it, and hooked it through the hoop; we were in the lead.

"Look at that! ... Wait, wait ..." The announcer detailed the attack of our rivals as they tied the score once more. Then several clean shots from my team bounced us back into the lead.

Abruptly, a rival player maneuvered, and lowered his shoulder knocking me to the floor. "Oooooh! That must have hurt," the announcer referred to my bleeding body. 2 minutes before the end of the game, the arena seemed to be on *black fire*. I beseeched the

26

coach to put me back into the game. After a moment of hesitation, his reluctant support transported me to the court.

Time Stopped!

Everything around me started to move in slow motion. I perceived the players' energy as they traversed the intricate spaces of the court.

Time accelerated again, the ball moved swiftly, and the scores were tied.

60 seconds to go. I jumped to shoot … and heard the agonizing scream of a rival player who tore his *Achilles heel*.

The clock offered *a choice*. The ball dropped … and a lad walked over to the wounded stranger to extend a helping hand. The game was over … we had *lost* … and catcalls echoed throughout the *coliseum*.

$$\infty$$

That night, the sky watched a lonely lad sitting on his roof. Making a wish, he plucked one of his eyelashes and blew it into space. Then … a familiar voice traveled his way …

"If you keep up your basketball speed, you might find yourself clashing against a canyon."

"Mother…" My eyes lit with joy. "Your speed is fast becoming common knowledge, my boy." She kissed me on the forehead, and her finger lifted my chin. "My light … blessed you are with bravery of the heart, yet in the face of fear, you flee to the stars. What do you say we go together and drink some fresh tea, huh?"

The mother's angelic hand reached down and pulled the boy up. And as they wandered off … his heart still contemplated the heavens.

$$\infty$$

At school, the young boys and girls grouped together in like minded bands, but a young, dark-skinned lad fell between the cracks. When the school's bell rang, a break began, and like a deserted painter, the boy colored his parchment with paradise, a place where colors live in harmony.

His wish to play with just one friend had not materialized until one day, towards the close of that 6th year of school, the sun's rays revealed a friend. For weeks, they played together. The heart of the

27

lonely lad was happy. Then, one school break ... his new companion no longer answered.

The lifeless corners of the school yard offered no clue as to the friend's whereabouts. And when the lad finally found his friend, the companion said: "I can't be your friend anymore ... I can join them ... but only if I leave you alone."

It seemed as though the lad had met a *dead end*. From that day on, every *Independence Day*, while youths were celebrating in the night, the lad would watch them from a little roof, shedding *tears* as shooting stars streaked across the dark sky above him.

Around the ages of 11 and 12, a happening *decided* to transpire. I felt as though my mind was floating in the ocean, hovering like a gyre. Subconsciously my mind *picked up* the science of semiotics, seeing worlds in a single grain of sand. My eyes began to *blink* frequently with new eyesight. And if one day I am summoned to the chamber of secrets to interpret this code ... I would write ... *An apparent misfortune ... is a gift in disguise.*

Accelerated Expansion of Time-Machine Imagination

Laying in bed listening to fairy-tales late into the night ... "To understand a tree, go to the molecular root," my mother sang. "Master the subtext of *your own* subconscious ... and you shall master all colors, archetypes, and innovations." The words were billowing like a white robe ...

There is no Time.
Break the gravity of your mind, curve the clock's chronicles.
And expand your mind to see a thousand years ahead.
See deep into the streets of history and the future, without losing your moral character.

So my mind hopped on a magical carpet and traveled many midnights to the passages of the past.

Dreams of the exotic East transported me to *Egypt*. The romance of Cleopatra and Marc Anthony painted a heart in the starry skies. I studied music and mummies. The battle of the

28

Pyramids led me to the secrets of the Rosetta stone, and I strove to decipher ancient Egyptian hieroglyphics.

From the minaret of Mecca dawned the call of the Azan, sounding the life of Saladin, the story the Black Stone, and the times when the crescent and the cross were in concord.

The myth of the warrior king, a medieval superman – King Arthur – arose from the Round Table in the North. A young boy challenged to heroically extract a sword from a stone, inspired expeditions to discover Camelot, the wizard Merlin, the Excalibur, and the Holy Grail.

One late afternoon, as I was playing with my collection of flags and coats of arms. Suddenly, an overlooked compartment slid open. Several tickets rattled within, like the tail of a snake. A stern voice made me swallow …
"What are you doing?" My mother's tone forbade a rubbish reply.
"ER – I …"
"You curious little child …"
"Mother, please tell that it is true … please …"
"Yes it's true … we are going to Greece."
"Yeah!" My spirit sprinted to my roof, and I held *The Iliad* and *The Odyssey* close to my heart, those epic revealing bridges between reality and the beyond through symbols.
Every night before the Greek adventure, I would lie in my bed, cuddled by the blankets and my *nightlight* …
Compelled by loads of excitement, I immersed myself in the tales of the Trojan War and Achilles. The Golden Fleece and the Chariot of Apollo inspired a naïve wish: "Would it be alright if you gave me a lift?"

Astrological symbolism, guiding the secrets of the stars, sparked the idea of *the 4 elements* and the story of Aristotle, a little pupil that outshined Plato … and passed on a new way of looking at the natural world to a young *transformed* prince by the name of … Alexander the Great.

The Island of Rhodes

Shaped like a spearhead, the island is dotted with many ancient villages warmed by an eternal spring, and on strips of land, grapes and olives grow freely.

After storming the rocky sea shores and playing under the sun, my family visited *the Acropolis* of Rhodes and the Palace of Grand Masters of the Knights of Rhodes.

"Yaso!" My father relished in the Greek cuisine. And while fish, olive oils, herbs and Kourabiedes were served, I asked the waiter: "Excuse me, dear sir, where might I find ambrosia or the elixir of life?"

The break of dawn discovered a young lad seeking one of the 7 Wonders of the Ancient World: *The Colossus of Rhodes*. A sonnet by Lady Lazarus, contrasting the Colossus with the Statue of Liberty, was engraved on a plaque …

Not like the brazen giant of Greek fame,
With conquering limbs astride from land to land;
Here at our sea-washed, sunset gates shall stand
A mighty woman with a torch, whose flame
Is the imprisoned lightning, and her name
Mother of Exiles. From her beacon-hand
Glows world-wide welcome; her mild eyes command
The air-bridged harbor that twin cities frame.
'Keep, ancient lands, your storied pomp!' cries she
With silent lips. 'Give me your tired, your poor,
Your huddled masses yearning to breathe free,
The wretched refuse of your teeming shore.
Send these, the homeless, the tempest-tost to me,
I lift my lamp beside the golden door!'

And so … the adventure to the island of Rhodes was over. Those who believe in myths might wake up in the morning blessed, only to find themselves cursed.

History repeats itself with a different dress; the Greek empire would become a Roman address. And if the lad hoped that his new school would be a *success* … well …

Alas

.

30

CHAPTER 8
The Ripples of the Domino Effect

When the sun's rays swept the planet every morning like a crystal glass shattering, I longed to unite with the flying creatures of the sky who sang of freedom.

"A fresh start," I hummed. "There will be new teachers and new students at the second stage of my schooling – a friend to love is on the horizon."

The hourglass of the first day funneled its sands … but no matter which chair the dark-skinned lad sat in, the other children acted as though it were empty.

The strings of his heart's violin snapped when students from the previous school started locking the gates of good *fate*.

And only then did he realize the reason. On the one hand, the children from the common class saw his tailored clothes as aristocratic … On the other hand, the elite, aristocratic class labeled the hybrid of wealth and dark skin as alien.

Chained in the prison of the *intellect*, the lad was afraid to go out on the school's breaks … finding safety with the old janitors … who had once befriended him when he was young.

One school recess, a white group from the elite class was ready to display their fury. The dark-skinned lad left the cafeteria carrying his food, when a student from the aristocratic house struck the boy's silver tray. "Oh … did I do that?" The student mocked. "I am terribly sorry indeed for my misdemeanor … let me make it up for you. Oy, Thomas! C'mere and help." 3 trolls hurried over and trampled the boy's bread. The bell rang and the gang leader growled: "I bid you farewell, blackie."

A strange sense of mist engulfed geography class. The teacher displayed a map of the world which provoked the lad to ponder: "How many more are paid these *pains*?"

His eye leaked a *tear* … and the child fled home to his roof. He shouted into the vastness of space, and that night a diary *cried* …

Dear Source of Light
    As clay in the hand of the potter
    As helm in the hand of the seaman
    As silver in the hand of the smith
    As stone in the hand of the mason
    So is one who has no sense of the Universe.
    I don't know if you can hear me or where you are…
    Yet a prisoner dares to ask, 'Shall my scars guide like stars?'
    For my tears rain with strangers' prayers yearning for thy
    Cane … as an outcast craving a single friend.

At the age of 13, I believed *the present* was slipping on a steep slope. I didn't know who I was. I thought I would never be someone … that touching the stars was reserved only for the aristocratic lords of the system. And so … I became a loner.

I lost interest in the school's classes. In sullen silence, I immersed myself in *the Tree of Knowledge* … the precious balance between the independence of the 13 colonies and the liberty of La Marianne. *The Book of Wisdom*, the voyage of the *Essex,* and Anna Karenina ascended the spiral staircase of my mind.

And after discovering the titans – those heroes of the past who freed their minds and *wrote the future* – I *decided* that the day would come … when I too would innovate and establish my life.

"But how will I do it?" I prickled with fear when I couldn't find the philosopher's stone.

A pair of double-doors revealed itself next to my *nightlight* … one door was titled **The Intellect System** … and the other door was named … **Time's Silent Secret.**

Enchanted by its glittering golden words … I opened the first door. And so I decided that the train of my future will take me to an Ivy League school; old institutions with astronomy towers, legendary halls, libraries, bewitched museums, and botanic gardens.

"There is no doubt," my mother whispered as she kissed me good night …

The Network of Energy … is not without a sense of irony …

32

CHAPTER 9
The Network of Energy

One views the currents of the river. The leaves fly in heavenly harmony. One hears the birds singing a symphony and feels the blades of the grass tickle in between the toes. Then suddenly, in a far away land, *a tear* shifts the world. Everything changes. And one says ...

> *Those who forget to see the future ... are those who can't see*
> *The butterfly in London ... flapping an earthquake*
> *In the **Black Sea**.*

One shining afternoon, when the sun was burning high in the sky, the entire circle of my family was gathered at my grandmother's quaint house. Lamb chops, steaks, boiled potatoes, carrots, roast potatoes, fresh bread and red wine were served on the round table.

A rare breed of Rottweiler dog was barking in the garden. Bigger than most dogs ... he rose his barks to roars, intruding upon the symposium of sounds around the table.

"Father, may I please go to Epi?" I asked.

"Are you crazy, lad? You'll be eaten alive! That dog can't be tamed."

"But father ... I ..."

"No! For once in your life obey me boy. This creature can't be controlled..."

A delicate wind started to seep through the cracked window pane. I took a plate and a cup ... and snuck away.

From the garden burst a tumult of terrifying barks. I began to descend the little hill as Epi reared, leapt, and circled around his leash.

Fury blazed in his eyes the closer I came to his hallowed zone. Then ... *time stopped*. Life started to flow in slow motion as the barks ebbed. Eye to an eye with Epi, I believed.

"I can feel your energy ... your *tears* are just hunger." I laid the steak and water on the grass, the dog was released, and together we played hide and seek. I glanced up at the little hill and saw Miriam, her scarf billowing in the breeze, shed a tear as she watched her son.

So the riddle remains ...

If a little meteor successfully splashes down in the midst
Of the sea … and no one hears it …
Does it ripple a sound?

6 months after I decided to pave my path to an Ivy League school, my mother was summoned for a parent-teacher conference. Since I was neglecting classes and suffering poor grades … I was afraid.

"Good morning, Miriam. You look so young!" my head-teacher Syra observed. "Yeesss … the boy has definitely got your eyes."

"Thank you, Mrs. Markon," Miriam replied.

"Oh please … call me *Syra*," she said condescendingly.

Looking at the dark-skinned lad, Syra asked, "Well, Omer … is there anything you want to say?" A sour face answered in silence.

"All right then," Syra cleared her throat. "The reason I summoned you here, my lady, is that we have quite a problem indeed. You see … your son is … quite an offbeat bird."

The lad's blood began to boil.

"One morning can deliver a shy, solitary student … yet the next day he is terribly passionate when he enters the class … like a bomb about to go off. He surprises me."

Miriam replied, "I understand."

"I will be frank. His abilities to study and make friends are very poor." The lad clenched his fist, which his mother soothed by gently taking his hand in hers. "Mrs. Markon," Miriam mediated. "Your words will be advocated."

"Good …" Syra granted and handed over a lumpy package of pumpkin pastries and peppermint to the lad.

As they were about to depart, Syra said: "Oh … and one more thing … tell him to stop spending his time with the janitors. This is a school, not the house of commoners."

The stars shone like white pearls as I watched them from my roof. My music box depicted a ship sailing in the skies towards a lighthouse. Like a *nightlight*, it lit the cold parapets of stone and *the rose* I was holding.

I heard my name called from within the house. I jumped to the adjacent terrace, then to the next, then glided on the railing and landed on the terrace facing the parlor.

"Can't you just come down the stairs for once?" David scolded.

My mouth went dry, and I announced,
"*I didn't break the roses' vessel!*"
My mother inquired, "How do you know it is broken?"

"At any rate…" my father continued. "I am well aware of your dream to go to one of these distant, wizardly schools that will supposedly spark magic in your life. But you are only at the second stage of your schooling. And you still need to go to the third. Therefore, we are bent on sending you to the best private tutors."

"They will hold me back," I countered.
"Always looking at the road ahead. Never living *the moment*," my mother sighed.
"What for?" I replied.
"It's *the painting paradox*. To see the road ahead, the panoramic view of the painting, you have to step back, be in the moment," Miriam enlightened.
"Don't be aloof boy, only a fool would refuse a *good fortune* that assists his future," hammered David .

My mother rose from the royal blue Alcantara chair. She approached her son. She bent down … and our heights aligned. "My light … your happiness is my hope in life. These tutors will root your legs in the ground, while your mind will fly in the sky. What do you say, my love? Let's do it together."
"Can one of these tutors be Aristotle or Confucius?" I asked.
"Well, I am not quite sure about that, but I promise you the rarest teachers."
"Alright mother. *To The Stars!*" And our hands met like 2 candle flames.

The Intellect System sent its goblins to persecute a dark-skinned lad with unbearable torments at school; the afternoons provided the warm meals a mother made for her child.

Street lamps, fields, and lanes flashed across the window as my mother drove late into the night to drop me off or pick me up from private tutors all across the land. I would train in the halls of the rarest teachers, learning Astronomy, Ancient Literature, World History, Quantum Science …

Life flew by fast, leaving my youth lonely. As my mother watched my broken face from the rear-view mirror, she would assure … "Winning one's future is a force of enlightenment. Future consciousness – is connected to the subconscious. And the subconscious is steered by emotions, not intellect.

The Intellect System shall lure your time through machines. But *times change* when one evolves and grasps the key to the subconscious.

> *So self-reliance boy ... self-reliance!*
> *I can only show you the door*
> *But*
> **YOU** *have to walk through it.* "

CHAPTER 10
The Color of the Air

Each Valentine's Day … a young lad would ascend to his roof and dream of being loved. Romeo and Juliet would find a place close to his heart as his pen would write….

Dear Source of Light
 Wishes fly to thee like falling stars after sunset
 Yet a roof is wet and someone is forgotten
 For my wish to gift my princedom to a pauper never
 Came… will love also claim shame?
 Many nights under the skies dome, Venetian lovers
 Roam … will a candlelight one day know their glow?
 A cheek is left all alone … still hopes to blush …
 Though Cupid's home is unknown

Then, one day, the dark-skinned lad fell in love. A girl with golden curls from the elite class captured his spirit with her snow white skin, ocean blue eyes, and ruby lips. Though his mother and father bore the *bad luck* of being raised by neglecting parents … they *decided* to *transform* the darkness into light by becoming the best parents they could be. Their son decided to *pick up* the lesson and swore never to play games that could hurt a girl's heart.

Dazzled by the girl's poetic beauty, the lad disclosed in a parchment …

I have been holding you in my thoughts
Close to my heart where beats the beauty of your brightness.
Every dawn, the birds fly and sing to you, your highness.
Your pearled grace traces the vase of my soul …
And may I have the honor … of inviting you for a stroll

P.S.
If your father's approval is called for …
Please let me know.

The next morning, the lad's eyes beamed with hope … Upon entering the school's gate, he discovered dozens of students seated in the courtyard, laughing as the golden girl cried out, parchment in hand, "Omer ... he is so amusing."

Love is colorblind. The stars of *light* do not leave the skies when their color turns ***dark at*** night."

Reflectively ...
One day, during the second stage of my schooling, a black man named Joan came to our home in hopes of climbing a small ladder to a brighter life.

My family extended their hearts, and Joan thanked the light. I bonded with him as a brother, and we would speak for hours on end.

Our minds traveled to the mystical affair between the Queen of Sheba and a King who built a Temple, and I asked Joan if he had seen The Ark of The Covenant ... as he drove down the roads of Africa, trying to avoid the potholes.

The last midnight he stayed with us, my mother held his first born daughter, *Miriam.* Joan stood at the center of the parlor beside his new wife and proclaimed ...

I say unto you today ...
Dream! Dream as though you shall live forever!
Each child has a star ... and I have reached mine ...
But without the spirit of humankind I wouldn't shine...
Thank you, and
May the Light guide you.

38

CHAPTER 11
Runway to Victory

My new dream to study at an Ivy League school was fueled by human beings' coins ... which paid for a *brighter future*.

A fresh *adventure* beckoned me towards the currents of the Atlantic Ocean when Miriam affirmed, "Son, this journey is for the purpose of your aspirations. Do not regard it by any means as a carefree game."

The Shores of America

The doors of the flying stallion opened, I jetted out, shouting the timeless line: "Give Me Liberty or Give Me Death!"
My mother caught up with me, smoothed my hair, and smiled.

Lady Liberty held her *torch* high, as a black taxi took us to a grand lodge. The gothic skyline was comprised of the worlds' largest skyscrapers. "Look, son," my mother said that night. "From afar ... it looks like the stars and stripes."

Sunrise and sunset came and went as I fell in love with all my *dreams*. My mother traveled with me to a magical place ... *a roof* by the river that she enjoyed when she lived in the Big Apple for several years. The scent of fresh bagels wafted up along with a song that took my breath away.

The next morning, an array of flags waved in *union* outside a bright building. They recalled how the rubble of **war** could *transform* into a palace of **peace**, which proclaimed to the planet:

Recognition of the inherent dignity and of the equal and inalienable
Rights of all members of the human family
Is the foundation of freedom
Justice and peace
In
The
World

A Greek myth transformed into a modern spectacle.

The wind carried us to a center in the heart of the city. A looming golden statue of ***Prometheus*** was atop a precious stone. Like a child hypnotized by a butterfly, I read the legend of Prometheus hidden on the granite wall ...

> *"Prometheus, teacher in every art, brought the fire to earth that hath proven to mortals a means to mighty ends."*

I watched the people gliding on the ice. It seemed as if thousands of candles were floating in mid-air.

A Tear began to glide from my eye. A child naively asked his mother, "If Prometheus brought fire to the world, and a scientist discovered E=MC^2 ... do you believe one day someone will give to the world *Time's Silent Secret*?"

"What is that, my light?"

"The Chariot of Champions ... *the power to write the future*."

"Well, my darling ... let's hope a tragedy doesn't break a heart before that happens."

The wind heard the lad's tears and whirled the mother and the child to a mystical museum.

There, the child saw a painting of a hero, *Crossing The Delaware* – a symbol of a human being overcoming obstacles and reaching *the stars*. Suddenly, the painting left the dark-skinned lad feeling all alone in the world. The gap between his *DREAMS* and reality seemed unbridgeable. And with a sad yet hopeful voice ... the child said to his mother ... "One day, mother ... *one day* will come ... when I will reach my star."

40

CHAPTER 12
Between the Column and the Star

Adopt a systematic study of the way
All things change into one another; pay
Constant attention to this aspect of nature
And train yourself in it.
Nothing is so conducive to greatness of Mind.
- MARCUS AURELIUS

Back at home ... I contemplated how to improve my grades in the second stage of my schooling ... for the dream of going to one of the oldest schools in the world.

Just as an astronomer sits in a room for days ... observing how the galaxy expands and changes ... I too decided to explore this *science of observation.*

Men always think that the universe is *there* ... instead of right *here.* I sat motionlessly on the highest tier of my roof, my eyes seeking to comprehend life's ever-changing flow through lenses of slow motion.

It seemed that wise owls were perched on infinite spiral staircases ... watching my every blink.

Suddenly ... *a child picked up* a principle.
I was mystified by my mother ... something didn't make sense. On the one hand, she wrote poems, played the piano, painted pictures, and performed spiritual healing. Yet on the other hand, she would effortlessly balance the bills and profits of our household.
"How could that be?" I asked, for rarely will the human mind encompass **opposites**.
"Artists shun the philosophies of money, whereas the goblins of the bank and money merchants are averse to the unseen risks of artistic pursuits. Spiritual people see quantum sciences as transient in time, while scientists see spirituality as foolish in substance." I whispered on my roof.

Fused to my chair ... I wrote a letter to my mother asking about this phenomenon. I folded the parchment into a little airplane and flung it into the air hoping that she would notice it. Then, a day later ... Miriam sent her letter of reply to my roof ...

A child wants to have X, Y, and Z ... and then to unite them.
An adult ... thinks in terms of either/or.
The mind's cosmic torch, the one The Intellect System tries to
imprison ...
breaks mental barriers ... and unites opposing powers.

"Quite right! Of course!" I said as my eyes widened in excitement. I took the pen and scribbled on a new parchment ...

Between the Column and the Star!

... the union of the Physical World (the Column) and the Spiritual World (the Star) ...
"But how does one do that?" I wondered. "How can a human drink from *The Fountain of Youth* and open the gates of the mind to unite opposite *powers*?"
It did not matter how much I prayed to the skies for a solution ... the Universe did not deliver the treasure.
    "So how shall I sharpen my scores at school and raise my grades?" I thought.
    "Wait a second!" I uncovered a lead. "Opposite powers require *resistance*. To evolve the muscles ... one's hands must pull the ends of the band in *opposite directions*.
So perhaps it is the same with the mind. If I **succeed** in solving all the *toughest* riddles and yet **fail** to answer the *easiest* ones ... I shall stretch my mind in opposite directions, creating resistance, and my mind – my reality – will *EVOLVE*."

42

CHAPTER 13
The Victor versus the Victory

At the end of the second stage of my schooling, an evening ceremony drew a large crowd of parents and children to celebrate.

Music, night shows, food, and lights closed the door of an era. After years of *failures* with friends and teachers fogging the way, a dark– skinned lad crouched in a lonely corner of the courtyard under the fireworks. He fell to his knees and *a tear* trickled from his eye, like sap sadly seeping from a tree. He looked to the heavens and whispered … "This moment is all I have to make my mother proud. All my youthful wishes were washed away … will you hear the heart of a crying child?"

The principal stepped up to the podium and spoke: "Ladies and gentlemen, distinguished guests, and my dear students. Every moment paves the way to our future. Here I hold a trophy, bestowed every year – not to the smartest student, but to the one who cared the most. Someone who clenched their teeth with perseverance when they felt too weary to carry forward. Indeed it makes no difference who the winner shall be … for it was my honor to be a part of your history."

The principal unfurled a parchment. The crowd waited with bated breath … and a name was called.

The happiness on my mother's face eclipsed my stage fright, and I briskly stepped up the stairs to the podium.
I held the trophy, looking at the light beaming from my mother amidst a cloud of contemptuous looks from the white aristocratic class.

But The Source of Light was there for me, and I was there for my mother, lifting the trophy in triumph … thanking her for believing in my *dreams*.

"Never stop climbing the mountain," Miriam said. "And when you reach the summit … that precious pinnacle … that is exactly the time to start *everything* all over again."

In the midst of that summer, to help me pursue my dream of entering an Ivy League school, my mother sent me to a majestic summer school in Great Britain.

In the nights before my impending adventure, I would sit on my roof beside my musical *nightlight* and listen to the echoes of the British Commonwealth …

> *… Horatio Nelson … Boudica … Cromwell … Uprising …*
> *…The Navy Fleets of Britannia … A New World …*
> *… The British Empire … Global Power …*
> *… The Great Fire of London …*

In the summer of my 15th birthday, I landed in London. The school's architecture was spectacular. A medieval institution with swooping lawns, large gardens, and sports fields. The campus was composed of different houses where it seemed orders of magicians might reside.

Paintings and portraits lined the walls of corridors, passageways, and *dark* tunnels … it was a subtle science to remember where anything was.

Before my arrival, I was afraid that once again … my dark skin would foil my chances of finding a friend. Yet to my great surprise, within a day, I was rather popular. Students from all over the globe dwelled in dorms, and an air of gallantry whirled from the marble floors and filled the stone halls.

3 days after my arrival, Cupid shot an arrow to my heart. Her name was Sophie Marie. Her dark brown hair, oval face, little nose and pearly brown eyes, captured my spirit … and I fell in love.

I composed sonnets night after night … that would be sent to her along with flowers of many shapes and colors. One night, I stood beneath her terrace and shouted, "Sophie!"
"Shhhh!" she admonished. "You'll wake the entire school."
When she descended to the courtyard, I said, "I want you to teach me how to waltz."
"Why?" she asked, implying the late hour of the night.
"Because no girl has ever danced with me before." She suddenly looked into my eyes and kissed me on the lips, and together we spent the night under the stars.

For the first time in my life on this planet, the color of my skin didn't cause silent storms ... *well, at least that's what I thought.*

One class, an Irish boy gave me a piercing look with his cold blue eyes. He was only 15, but his receding hairline, shaped his scalp like a spear. His white face had a pinkish hue, and his beard grew like a Viking forest. Subconsciously, we recognized a connection ... our eyes blazed with flames.

After the class drew to a close, the students were walking down the grand hall. Leaning against the wall in his long black coat, he called: "Hey you!" I turned, and the Irish lad hissed loudly, "Over here ... " After looking around warily, I approached him, and he said, "Come... take a walk with me."

The boy's name was John. He started a chat that would last 6 hours ...

"Cricket, rugby, driving on the left ... all is boring. What do you say we try a new game? Something more ... competitive, shall I say."

Over an ice-cold drink, he proposed a simple game: 2 bands of youths are battling one another with wooden clubs and blunt broom sticks.

I looked around at the splendid diversity of races and colors of the students. I then said to John: "Let's enlighten the game a little."

After scanning the schoolyard, pointing out spots, predicting pitfalls and scribbling on piles of papers ... we set the game.

The Game's Name: *Earth's Civil War*
The Goal: *Winning 5 continents of Earth*
The Armies: *John's Team shall lead the North. Omer's Team shall lead the South*
Number of Matches: *5 battles for 5 continents*

A game where John would assemble the Northern students: Irish, British, Swedish, Canadian, German, Scottish, Finnish ... And a dark-skinned lad would assemble the Southern students: Italian, Spanish, African, Portuguese, and South Americans.

It was an idealistic war. A war between the British maritime fleet and the desert warriors of the Sahara. A war between the glory of the Austrian orchestra and the solo Spanish guitar. A war ... between North and South.

The Declaration of Earth's Civil War.

The Rules:

1. *The leaders shall decide upon the time and place of the battle. Communication through letters only.*

2. *The weapons comprise clubs and blunt broom sticks. No cursing, kicks or fists are allowed.*

3. *New Southern and Northern fighters can join their army at any time.*

4. *Prisoners shall be taken only if: A) A Weapon falls. B) The fighter falls.*

5. *Prisoners shall fight for the opposing team. No leader can be taken prisoner.*

6. *Lady Victory, a mutually approved girl, shall be given 5 golden keys. Each key represents a continent. A key will be given to the winner of each battle.*

7. *The winner of 3 battles is the winner of the war.*

There was one more secret provision. John and I used some strange looking coins and purchased a golden crown in the form of a laurel wreath. We hid it in a forgotten corner of the medieval school and decided that the victor of the war would be crowned emperor by the loser.

Then John said, "I want to be the Duke of Wellington."
A shock wave flooded the banks of the body, and I whispered …

Waterloo …

"What?" John checked.
"N-nothing," I mumbled. "I will be Napoleon."
John flipped a coin. It hit the grass. John won, and the first 2 battles were his to devise.
We shook hands … and a lad declared, "Let's rewrite history."

46

News of the war swept the medieval campus … and the armies' collective subconscious was ignited.

The Battle for Australia

The courier came along carrying a letter signed by John.

To the Southern Army…

> *-The Battle for Australia*
> *-Noon*
> *-Field number 2*

The Southern Army had recruited 55 fighters, and John's team, the Northern Army, had amassed 45 fighters, when we convened on the battlefield exactly as the clock pointed its hands to noon.

The clouds began to divide in the heavens above where the Northerners were already stationed at the requested field. Out in front, John stood firm and grinned at the advancing Southerners.

I spotted a fault in the strategy of the North. While I wore simple clothing so as to be one with my fighters, John dressed up like a royal prince, alienating himself from the rest of his army.

The wind was blowing, the Network of Energy was moving, and John shouted, "For Glory!" He raised his broom-stick high toward victory.

The Northern fighters echoed his battle cry, the ground shook, and like roaring rhinos … they ran toward us.

Less than 10 minutes later, I called retreat … and the battle was over. John took 15 prisoners and said, "This is going to be easier than I thought."

Lady Victory, a girl in a pink dress with porcelain skin and brown hair … came by, emanating an air of nonchalance and grace. She awarded John a golden key and floated away like a spring leaf.

A Southern fighter passed by me, and I said, "Time is endorsing another team today."

The Battle for Africa

The South had lost Australia, and now the courier announced the battle for Africa. John was aware of my love for this continent and decided to strike where it would hurt. The battle would be 1 hour before *sunset* at field Number 1.

The South had only 40 fighters, while the North had 60.

The Southern Army arrived on time at the chosen battlefield, only to find it empty. I was surprised, for John was a Swiss watch – always on time.

As we waited for the Northern Army, which far outnumbered ours, my forehead began to gather drops of sweat in anticipation of the impending danger. Then … we saw them marching.

John was a jaguar on the hunt. He led his army with an austerity and a possessed look on his face.

A *freezing fear* made me gulp, when I calculated that some new fierce Northern fighters had joined his advancing army.

John signaled with his hand. The Northerners stopped moving. *Cold rage* streamed from John's soul. He drew his weapon from its scabbard … and silently charged alone toward us in attack.

In less than 5 minutes, I shouted retreat. The battle was over. The Southern Army had lost 10 fighters. John approached and, grinning at my amazement, taunted, "The crown calls my name."

Lady Victory swung by … and awarded John another golden key. "Until next time …" he smirked, condescendingly doffing his chapeau … and taking off into the *twilight*.

The Battle for Asia

I had fought poorly, and the Southern soldiers had become the laughing stock of the campus.

In my dorm, I looked over the map of Planet Earth … the South had lost the continents of Australia and Africa. Though it was my turn to devise the next 3 battles, I knew that John's Northern Army had the upper hand, for if they scored one more victory, they would win the entire war.

"What will I do?" I asked myself as I paced back and forth in my dorm. "The Southern soldiers now number only 30, while the Northern Army is comprised of close to 80 fighters." I was calculating possible actions when a mole came to alert me that 10 more fighters had joined John's army.

This moment of *tragedy* created a sense of emergency … and with it … several powerful realizations

48

"I should have never thought that because I *designed* the *game*, victory would naturally be mine," I whispered while writing out the thoughts.

I then comprehended that if I continue to rely on sheer force, I would stand no chance, for John *logically* saw the game as war, while I conceived of it as a *child-like* poem or a type of mystical science.

But right then, a solution surfaced in my consciousness: "If John uses brute force ... I will use *the mind*."

Military warfare is a subconscious warfare.
Several Southern fighters and I approached the school's chefs and tried to convince them not to cook food for the Northern Army.
"How will we tell who is who?" one chef inquired.
"Just look at the color of the skin." one Italian fighter replied.
To put it mildly ... the plan failed.

That night, as the crescent moon hung like a pearl earring in the sky, I took some books from the library, laid them on the grass in a circle, and sat in the center.
The battles of Frederick the Great and a young prince from Corsica were opened for my eyes to study. After meditating for hours ... my mind *picked it up* and I composed a plan on a parchment.

John's *intellect* led him to blindly think that because the Northern fighters had a mental advantage of widespread popularity and greatly outnumbered the Southern Army ... he would finish us off just by showing up at the battlefield.

"Fernando!" I called to a near-by Southern fighter.
"Prepare for battle ... we are going to turn someone's pride upon him."

There is an ancient adage that says: "Never attack your enemy from 4 sides." The wisdom implies that if the enemy is *tragically* distressed from all sides, he will *transform* ... and fight for his life with an unbeatable force, since he has no escape route.

That's exactly what the Southern Army needed.
The mental state of the Southern fighters was distressed. To spur their spirits onwards, *a tragedy* was needed to further lower their mental state, so that their minds would be set free, allowing them to fight for triumph.

"But how shall I cause the Northern Army to attack the Southern fighters from 4 sides?" I pondered.

The Quenching Square ...

First, for 2 nights, the Southern Army would train *themselves* to arrange a square shape on the battlefield.
Then, the ace was unleashed ... On these nights, I sent allied students around the medieval campus to ascend the school's roofs and drop off missives ...

The Northern Fighters Are Gods ...
***Do Not** Attack The Southern Army by Creating a Square Shape!*

□

John sent his spies to the Southern camp. He was informed that the Southern fighters were training to attack by creating a square. After John read the first line of the missive, his pride propelled him to do the exact opposite of what the missive advised.

Time smiled ... and reality was reshaped.

7:00 PM
On edge of magic, the Southern Army and I arranged ourselves in the shape of a square on the chosen battlefield. Like a lonely wolf, the sky looked down upon us while we waited for the Northern Army. Looking up at the divided clouds, I thought, "If John attacks us from the front ... all hope is gone, and the war is over."
Then suddenly ... my eyes welcomed the vision of the Northern Army as they advanced forward in 4 giant divisions, creating a square, *closing in*, dwarfing the smaller square of the Southern Army.
The Southern fighters' *distress* fogged their faith and continued to escalate *more* and *more* ... When John was about to give the signal to attack, the searing pain soared even higher ... and a Southern fighter screamed to the heavens:

"FOR FREEDOM!"

The Southern square stormed the Northern square with a great force. Wooden clubs and broom sticks *transformed* into clashing swords.

50

John cried retreat from the longest battle yet. The Southern Army cheered with liberty, and Lady Victory swung by ... awarding a golden key.

The Battle for America

I still found some time to devote to Sophie. I wrote to her of how much I loved her and showered her with kisses.

The school's classes didn't matter anymore. Our minds expanded beyond the school's walls and became consumed with winning the war.

The Northern Army won the continents of Australia and Africa, while the Southern Army had won the continent of Asia, leaving the score at 2 to 1 with the North in the lead.

John had lost almost 30 Northerners in the last battle, leaving each army with close to 70-80 fighters.

It was still my turn to devise the next battle, and I reflected on the fact that the game had become more violent: a swordfight of bruises and wounds. One bites from the apple ... and thinks that the future is immune.

"Victory is still in jeopardy," I thought to myself in the dorm. "For if the Northern Army wins just one more battle ... the war is over."

Looking over at The Declaration of Earth's Civil War ... I discovered a loophole. The Declaration did not restrict the soldier's weaponry to wooden clubs and wooden sticks. "*Wait ...*" I pondered, "perhaps other weapons may be used too." I made a note on my road map for the battle.

Moving quickly ... the Southern Army succeeded in securing 10 paint ball guns, yet the guns alone were not enough. "How will we use them?" a Southern fighter asked.

Meditating on the grass under the twilight, I reached into my pocket and withdrew a *green bill*. On its back was the pyramid with the all-knowing eye, *watching* from the apex. The past flashed before my eyes, and I sighed ...

The Battle of the Pyramids ... Egypt

For the rest of that night, 10 southern fighters trained themselves tirelessly to arrange into the shape of a triangle on the battlefield.

51

We set 2 simple rules upon marching to battle. The first stated that the Southern fighters should shoot only at the legs, not the bust or belly. The second stated that the bullets should be aimed to fly at the Southern fighters taken captive. "Why would we attack our own fighters?" some Southern *brothers* wondered. I replied, "A wounded yet *passionate* fighter… is worlds more powerful than a healthy one who lacks passion."

4:00 PM

10 southern fighters were arranged in a simple line. The sunny day waited for the enraged Northern Army.

When John and his fighters arrived, they were puzzled by the sight of 10 Southern fighters standing still, hands folded behind their backs.

"Omer, you coward!" John yelled. "Come on … show yourself!" John unsheathed his wooden club from its scabbard and commanded the North to storm. One Southern fighter shouted, "Break off!" The 10 fighters quickly arranged themselves in the shape of a triangle … and started to shoot at the opponents.

Any sensible commander would have run for his life, but John wanted to put up a good fight. Holding his position, he ordered the North to encircle the triangle and close in with a massive force.

Soon enough the plan failed … and when the Northern Army began to back away, opposite to the direction they had come from, I gave the signal. The rest of the Southern Army emerged from the forest and *surprised* the North with a sudden onslaught. John bellowed retreat and, in a reproachful rage, lunged forward to hit me as some fighters held him back.

Lady Victory floated forward, awarded a golden key, and after some curses and flying fists among the fighters … we never used the guns again.

The Battle for Europe

Each army had won 2 continents. The score was 2 – 2. The battle for Europe was the decisive fight – the winner would take all.

The North had lost 20 fighters, and with new fighters joining the South every minute … for the first time, we had the mental advantage.

15 Minutes before Dawn.

The entire Southern Army was dressed in black. We had recruited some musicians to play drums and trumpets as the march proceeded forward. A long triangular flag with the symbol of the circle was bathed in the ominous light emanating from the Southern fighters' flaming torches.

The South was chanting, "For Freedom … for Freedom …" The final moments before the dawn brought with them an impenetrable mist. The fog was so dense that both armies could barely see 10 steps ahead.

As the sun began to rise, the chants and the light of the torches started to materialize out of the mist. John later told me that one of his aides said: "They come from *Hell* …"

And John replied, "No … they come from *freedom*."

10 minutes later … the battlefield fell silent. Earth's Civil War was over. Lady Victory swung by and awarded the South the last golden key.

As a noble prince … John came to shake the hand of a dark-skinned lad. We first looked at one another … and the hand-shake *transformed* into a brotherly hug.

Sophie ran to embrace me, and I said to the fighters, "Brothers, we might have failed the school's tests … but we have proven the bravery of our hearts."

That night … there was one more promise to be kept between me and John – the loser was to crown the winner emperor.

We picked up the golden laurel crown hidden in a lonely corner of the Victorian campus … and walked quite a way to the nearest cathedral.

Approaching the altar, John joked, "Maybe we can do the coronation banquet at Westminster Abbey."

As John lifted the crown high up, the image of Alexander in Babylon was tempered by an *angel's touch*. My mother's voice echoed in my mind, and I recalled the observation of Abraham Lincoln …

… Nearly all men can stand adversity …
But if you want to test a
Man's character
Give him
Power

I took the laurel wreath from John's hands. I told him to close his eyes. When he opened them, he found the crown on his head. Perplexed, he asked,

"What? Why? ... You are the victor."

"Your *Failure*," I replied, "is greater than my victory." And I bowed before my friend.

With the heart of the romance left behind, Sophie's goodbye was like a kiss from the sun. The magical stallion came to pick me up and fly me home. On the way, I ingrained this adventure in my heart and decided that I would one day *transform* my name to James.

When I landed I ran into my mother's arms and thanked her so much. She asked: "How was summer school, Son? ... Were you on time to the classes?" With a mischievous recollection, I answered: "Well, Mother ... there was a little game that played with the times and classes."

CHAPTER 14
Tragedy and Transformation

Out of the ashes of the second stage of my schooling, rose the ice age of the next. Catering to the sons and daughters of the wealthiest aristocratic families … the third stage of my school was a finishing stage, turning *youths* into *adults*.

My 3 year-long dream of studying in an Ivy League school zoomed forward when I was accepted into the Honors Class. With almost zero effort, each elite student there would get the highest grades. Seeing all the fair-skinned students, my mother said, "Son, one thing is certain … you are going to add some color."

Not long ago, I had many diverse friends in London. And now … the loneliness of division drifted back to hound me.

Luxurious jewelry, custom made dresses, giggles, and fancy celebrations … all had evolved. And whenever a dark-skinned lad tried to visit … the door would close in his face.

Secluded on my roof, overlooking the magical green field, I wrote …

> *Cursed to be alone among all living things…*
> *I ascend to my roof to dream and count the stars by myself*
> *And let my eyes spill all the sadness of my heart.*
> *Walking alone in the valley of death, searching for*
> **Time's Silent Secret**
> *No doubt I shall never discover it …*
> *For I have no destiny in this world.*

It was a ***Tragedy*** … that would set my mind ***Free***.

A Tale of Two Fairies

A long time ago, in a faraway land, two young sisters were abandoned by their parents. Miriam and Anet grew up without a real home. The tiny dorm in the cold orphanage was their shelter against the rain and the darkness.

As the older sister, Miriam couldn't afford to long being a daughter to anyone. So she became the mother of her little sister.

Together they milked the cows every dawn … and prayed every sunset for a better life, and the wings to fly to happiness.

One afternoon, the classmates mocked the dark-skinned lad's poor grades and geeky look. Their lips curled in a sneer, crushing his hopes. And the lad headed home.

In the grand parlor … Anet was crying on Miriam's shoulder … and the lad departed to the roof, slamming the door with such a force that it swung off its hinges and landed flat on the floor.

As he sat there upon the roof … his mother came to comfort him. "What happened, my light?" she asked in her tender voice. "I am tired, mother. I have no friends … I am so lonely. How can I possibly believe that I will reach my star one day?"
"With time … The Source of Light will make everything right."
"No! I want The Source to do what I want now!" The child began to cry…
"I wish time would die … I wish space would die … I even wish that Anet would die."

Miriam rose abruptly and said, "Be careful of what you wish for, young one." She looked at her crying son … and left the roof.

The lad's head was bowed when the sound of footsteps lifted his sight.
"Anet …" he whispered under the pictorial stars of that night. Anet approached her nephew. "My darling, what's wrong? … What does your heart say?"
"Something in school … I just feel this unbearable burden that I must carry … and I am just a child." The lad looked up at his aunt.
"Don't lose hope, my love. Fear leads to bad choices, and bad choices become darkness," she said while caressing his hand.
"I want you to do me a favor, darling … Will you do it for me?" she asked.
"Yeah … "
"Your mother is my mother. She loved me all my life. I ask you to always love her. She believes in you more than you can dream."
"I promise, Anet. Why were you crying before?" the lad asked.
"Oh it was nothing darling, what's important now is you.
Remember…
The Source of Light will always guide you to the stars. Give me a

56

kiss now." The lad kissed her on the cheek, and Anet kissed him on the forehead.

The Turn of the Millennium.

2 days later, as I was sitting on my roof, my *nightlight* was playing along with the solemn sparkles of the stars, and the pillar-like trees stood darkly in the distance.

Suddenly, a harsh metallic note of shattered glass disrupted nature's symphony. I cautiously walked to my room. In my bathroom, shards of glass were strewn across the marble floor. Walking closer, I saw the wall clock floating in the bathtub in slow motion. It was like looking at the dimension of time through the reflection of the moon on the ocean.

Right then, Miriam entered my room and said …
"Anet is missing."

11:50 PM
The entire household was sitting in the parlor. Lost in a labyrinth of fear, I sat above the others on the stairs leading to the terrace.

The clock was ticking along with the beating of our hearts … when suddenly the phone rang, thundering louder than the rainstorm outside.

The ringing reverberated through the parlor. David dared to pick it up. A black cloud of doom shrouded David's face. The Clock sounded its last tick, the phone clashed against the floor … and the house burst into *tears*.

Miriam lowered her head as silent tears streamed from her motherly eyes. Then … she shouted to the heavens … but no sound emerged.

Shock left her speechless … *time stopped*! And a *lonely tear* fell from Miriam's eye, as a letter stained with tears was delivered to the gates.

Guilt threatened to tear my heart from my chest.

I ran to my room. I grabbed my collection of flags and coats of arms.
I stormed to my roof and dashed them to the floor.

In the pre-dawn light that painted the world, Miriam discovered her son soaking wet and shivering on the roof.

She quickly maneuvered through the flags and coat of arms strewn across the floor and asked, "My light, what happened here?" The child couldn't speak.

The mother put her hand on her son's forehead. "You are *burning* ..."

Miriam began to cry and hugged her child, "Come ... we need to prepare for the funeral."

CHAPTER 15
THE EQUATION

"What have I done?" The guilt ate at my heart as I didn't attend the funeral. My mother's orphaned sister, my loving aunt, had died. All her dreams vanished unfulfilled.

This *tragedy* triggered a subconscious *transformation* in me. I realized that the greatest disease, since the sun first shone upon the Earth, has been the failures of human beings to be whole – to reach their stars – to fulfill their dreams.

A series of urgent questions started to surface …

Why can't every human grasp success?
Why can't one have the powers of da Vinci, Newton, Beethoven, and Copernicus?
What inspired the greatest minds to innovate history?

It was clear, as the dawn swept the darkness off the streets, that the answer lay beyond "work hard", "keep your nose to the grindstone", "never give up", "clench your teeth", "endure" …

Of course all these adages have weight, but no one ever says, "To be successful, you need to breathe!" Obviously, without oxygen … how shall you stand a chance?!

Then, a profound wonder arose within me… "*How can it be that thousands of years have gone by, yet there is no Equation that explains life and the science of accomplishment?*" I began to understand that this Equation runs in the DNA of the Universe, and is a millennia-old treasure hidden in the margins of history.

2 stories inspired me to embark upon the expedition. The first was the story of a young British mathematician.

For *300 years*, minds had tried to solve Fermat's Last Theorem. Fermat had written in the margin of his book that he had a marvelous solution, yet he never put the proof on paper.

Many years later, a young mathematician locked himself in his home, determined to discover Fermat's solution. Then one day, he stood on a podium … and presented the solution.

The second story … was the myth of Prometheus.

And though for every Promethean action there is a Pandora's box of punishment … I decided to set sail and discover *Time's Silent Secret – The Equation*.

A Peek into the World's Consciousness

The human mind thinks that the Universe is *there*, that larger-than-life things are *there*, instead of seeking them *here*.

I didn't need to pack any bags, carry any water canteens, or travel to the desert to discover *The Equation*. My little room was just fine for this journey.

However, before I could continue … I needed to peek into the world's consciousness. One must know before one stands …

Dusting off archaic books, I began reading the *Analects* by Confucius, *Creative Evolution*, *Silent Spring*, and ancient scriptures like the *Vedas*.

Inspired by spirituality, powered by science, and *proven* by history … A butterfly waving its wings in London … will cause a tornado in China. All living things and numbers are interconnected and intertwined.

The world's consciousness is a cauldron of energies – common themes and powers that change the lives of people.

Every decision made by any human affects the dynamics of the world's consciousness.

As a child picks up a flower, so I picked up a timeline that shed light and captured the world's consciousness…

8,000 years separate the Agricultural and Industrial Revolutions.
120 years separate the Industrial Revolution and the light bulb.
90 years separate the light bulb and the landing on the moon.
22 years separate the landing on the moon and the worldwide web.
9 years separate the worldwide web and the sequencing of the human genome.

Machines and technology have enriched the global networks, creating more success stories and innovations, bestowing more breadwinners to the world. Flying the skies, cruising the oceans, surfing on the Internet … all have blurred the borders between nations.

The time it takes to produce and distribute an artistic or scientific creation has shrunk.

Nevertheless, the time saved is also *lost*. If innovators or artists save several months in production, those same months will be wasted as they try to arrange a meeting with a buyer. If the purpose of a creation is to be out in the world … What good is it to create if no one is inspired?

Back in history, arranging a meeting was easy … just a matter of showing up or knocking on a door. Yet today, despite all the progress … it takes months. And when the meeting does finally take place, the buyer is haunted by the ticking clock … and then board members wonder, "Why are profits down?"

As connected as the world has become, it has been stretched apart. Contracts have replaced a trustworthy word. Contacts have replaced friends. The home's shutters are shut so that no stranger will ask for favors. The plane travels to many cultures, yet one does not merge with these cultures. And sometimes the shine of the shoe is more important than the shoemaker.

Despite this *accelerated expansion* of progress … How many know who they are? Just walking down the street, how many can see their future?

Looking at the papers on my table, I saw the frantic rate of change displayed by the timeline, an acceleration that could easily cause one to feel lost, shocked and out of control of life. This mental state affects one's ability to make good decisions among such a rapid influx of information. It is like putting a 10-volt plug into a 10,000-volt outlet.

Night came along. Alone in my room, watching the view from the window … I wrote that technology and machines are there to inspire one to do what is hard, not what is easy. The same accelerated expansion should be channeled into the craftsmanship of one's character. One ought to see, deep into the streets of the future and achieve the genius to build global bridges, for machines can connect … but *union* depends on us.

The city was still asleep. The early beams of sunlight playing upon my window guided me along the path to discover *The Equation*.

Sitting at my wooden desk, I concluded that, after peeking into the world's consciousness, the expedition could move forward.

The empires of the future … are the empires of the mind
– WINSTON CHURCHILL

That line was a mystical clue on the map. For evolution to occur, first the walls blocking the mind must fall … so the eyes can see more clearly. As one futurist said, "The illiterate of the 21st century will not be those who cannot read or write; they will be those who cannot learn, *unlearn*, and relearn."

So the quest for *The Equation* continued … but first I had to unlearn the walls of my mind.

I began to read whatever classical memoirs I could get my hands on. I perused Plutarch's Parallel Lives, examined the characters of great men, and read scrolls on pragmatism. Slowly, I started to see … *what everyone else already knows.*

No Luck

Fortune favors the bold. – ARISTOTLE

Every man is the architect of his own future. – SALLUST

It is a great piece of skill to know how to guide your luck. – BALTASAR GRACIAN

Great men become great because they were able to master luck. – NAPOLEON BONAPARTE

Diligence is the mother of good luck. – BENJAMIN FRANKLIN

I find that the harder I work, the more I have it. – THOMAS JEFFERSON

The man who is intent on making the most of his opportunities, is too busy to bother with luck. – B.C. FORBES

Maybe I am lucky to be going slowly, because I may be going in the wrong direction. – ASHLEIGH

There were times I met luck at every turn. But luck is the good fortune you determine for yourself. – MARCUS AURELIUS

Once upon a time, on an unknown day, *The Intellect System* – the intellect of men – decided to infuse fictional stories into the world's consciousness. Socrates used to call these popular beliefs "bogies" … things which are used to frighten children.

And today, one of these fictional stories, Luck, is ingrained in the mind: blind luck, lucky, out of luck, wish you luck, a lucky break, beginner's luck, good luck.

The Intellect System sensed that the individual dislikes one thing … responsibility.

Upon hearing men whisper, "It is out of my hands," and, "I tell you that my neighbor is lucky, *not me*," all while pointing fingers in the blame game, *The Intellect System* saw a gap in the marketplace, and *Luck* was invented. In the ancient lands of the Middle East, many intuitively view "luck" as a matter of channeling energies, playing with them … like a chess game.

A man who works hard buys a new car.

His neighbor says, "Look at him. Why is he so lucky and I am not? I hope his car explodes."

The hard-working man uses his third eye and feels the wishes of his neighbor. Knowing that every wish can come true, he anticipates the future and prevents the inevitable … he scratches the car a little. The next day the neighbor says, "Yes! You see … justice is done. Now I feel lucky. Let me now see to my other neighbors …"

"The same transcendent game of energies plays out in card games," I wrote on the parchment. The wisest players believe not in luck, but in their own hands. With laser-like focus, they issue vast amounts of energy into the deck of cards, manipulating with their minds which cards will be drawn, and reshaping reality with *the decision* to become the gods of risk.

If I have ever seen farther, it is by standing on the shoulders of giants.
– ISAAC NEWTON

Success is a necklace composed of many individual diamonds. Every accomplishment comes about largely because of an investment made generations before.

Without Leo Tolstoy and Ghandi, no young man would have said, "I Have a Dream." And without this young man, and a bill signed by Lincoln, an athlete named Jordan would not have flown like an eagle.

"Without the pen of Thomas Paine, the sword of Washington would have been wielded in vain." – John Adams ... and no man would ever have set foot on the moon.

Without Isaac Newton, there is no E=MC². And there is no Galileo Galilei without the heavenly revolution of Copernicus.

As I sat at my desk *in my parent's home* ... some passages from history flashed before my eyes.

Van Gogh sold only one painting in his lifetime. A young actor who *transformed* into the President of U.S.A. first had 2 unsuccessful runs for the presidency. When Bell's telephone was struggling to get started, the owners offered the rights to buyers who pronounced, "What use could this company make of an electric toy?"

Are all these human beings Lucky or not?

The concept of luck is primarily a matter of how one perceives reality. 2 human beings are saved from a burning building. The first one says, "Thank you humankind. Thank you, Universe. I will be able to see my family again ... and swim in the ocean." The second one says, "Damn you all. I am so unlucky! I lost all my files in the fire."

As the wise Roman philosopher Marcus Aurelius wrote in his magnum opus, *Meditations* ...

> *'It is my bad luck that this happened to me.' No,*
> *You should rather say; 'it is my good luck'...*
> *Why we see more misfortune in the event than good fortune*
> *in your ability to bear it?...*
> *So in all future events which might cause sadness, remember*
> *to call this principle: 'This is no misfortune, but to bear*
> *It true to yourself is good fortune.*

The clock struck 8:00 PM, and a voice traveled from the parlor to my room: "Son ... how many cubes of sugar do you want in your tea?"

A eureka moment! I interpreted that luck is also a matter of precision and *details*.

If one wants to shine like the sun ... one must first study the kindled candle. When one *decides* to embrace precision, picking up forgotten details ... slowly one can predict future events. If one does

64

not know every aspect of what one is doing, down to the very last paper clip, one should anticipate some unwelcome surprises.

When a person falls close to the finish line, knowledge of the details was forgotten along the way. As Mr. Lehrer said: "Life is a sewer – what you get out of it depends on what you put into it."

During the late hours of the night … I was awakened by the call of an owl, and a skeptical mind wondered, "Wait … what about those who were born into wealthy families … isn't that luck?"
The author of How to Achieve Greatness answered: "The finest gifts of Nature are often found in persons of very humble families."

Opening one of the compartments of my desk, I glanced at the memoirs from oligarchs, to rock stars, tech tycoons, and glorious artists … Most of them came from poor, broken families filled with *tragedies*.

Then the voice asked, "What about beauty?" And I wrote: "Just look at the greatest human beings that ever lived. Not even one looks like Apollo or Aphrodite."
My journey to discover *The Equation* steered its sails. The wind crossed the Stars, carrying me forward … and the walls blocking my mind began to fall.

Luck has a new look …

No Talent

When *The Intellect System* saw that luck was dying, it said, "Let's try something new." Day and night, *the Intellect System* worked on the structure and promotion, and a new fictional story was manufactured … Talent.

The story of innate talent is equal to the concept of the emperor who paraded down the streets in his new clothes. Everyone was cheering … until a child shouted, "*But he isn't wearing anything at all!*"

As with the color of success, talent is never innate or inevitable, but achieved through *decisions* and one's mental ability to steer the subconscious.

The state of talent is the state of *disadvantaged* human beings … who *transformed* into masters.

Through the open window of my room, delicate wind flipped the pages of history before my eyes …

The scientist who discovered E=MC² didn't speak until he was 4-years-old and did not read until he was 7. One teacher described him as "mentally slow, unsociable and adrift forever in foolish dreams."

The man who created Mickey Mouse was fired by a news editor because "he lacked imagination." He went bankrupt before he built an empire based on imagination.

Winston Churchill failed 6th grade. And after failing in almost every election for public office ... he became prime minister at the age of 62.

A young inventor named Thomas had 1,000 unsuccessful attempts before he created the light bulb.

The man who freed the slaves in America was first *defeated* and *defeated* and *defeated* in almost everything his soul desired.

When a human being is born ... *a seed* of *destiny*, a vessel of energies, is installed in the infant's mind.

As one grows, *little sparks* of abilities are revealed. However, these little sparks merely guide one toward *unlocking and utilizing these and other lasting powers; a phenomenon that transpires only when one decides to take charge of the future for which one wishes.* For if not, these little sparks disappear like they never existed.

Lasting powers (Second Natures) never emerge...
Before one writes the future.

These little sparks... these abilities, are but snap-shots of the infinite moment, drops in the ocean – when compared to the endless powers stored in the mind. If one avoids taking charge of the future one wants, these little sparks trick one into believing in talent in the morning, only to negate it after the attacks of the afternoon.

True talent is a genius state of mind built and forged over time, as proven by the astronaut who perpetually practices.

Genius is one percent inspiration ... ninety nine percent
perspiration.
– THOMAS EDISON

"If innate talent is not an illusion, why then does it depend on people's taste and senses?" The map of *The Equation* revealed a clue.

Thomas Jefferson, an enlightened thinker, was labeled "an infidel … and a howling atheist … with fangs."

A young black actor named Sidney, was told: "Why don't you stop wasting people's time and go out and become a dishwasher or something?"

The teachers of the inventor of the light bulb said he was "too stupid to learn anything."

Beethoven was called by his teacher "hopeless, as a composer."

As I sat in my room beneath the light bulb, a realization arose. "What worth does 'talent' have if not *transformed* into innovation?" As Thomas Edison said: "I have more respect for the fellow with a single idea who gets there, than for a fellow with 1,000 ideas who does nothing."

When we see human beings bring their dream to life after years of sacrifice and good decisions, we say: "Oh … that's because she or he was was born talented."

The magnificent words of Emerson's essay "Self-Reliance" whisper: "In every work of genius we recognize our own rejected thoughts; they come back to us with a certain alienated majesty."

Suddenly, I started to see the letters $M - O - Z$ *everywhere*. Every page my eyes turned to … these letters seemed to be illuminated. "What does this mean?" I asked myself as the cold mists of the night crept through my window.

My knee hit a secret compartment of my desk, I pulled back in pain … and a book was revealed … $M - O - Z - A - R - T$.

Using a magnifying glass to zoom into the subtext of every line, I realized that Mozart's genius is not proof of innate talent that lasts forever, but rather evidence of an ancient concept begun centuries ago …

Press It On.

Press It On is a powerful concept whereby a parent presses on all failed or subconscious ambitions to a child through grooming and training.

This enforced training takes place from the time the child is born. And the child *picks the power up* and transforms it into a second nature, just as most children pick up a mother tongue ... *effortlessly.*

Press It On happened not only with Mozart, but also with an ambassador who groomed each of his sons to become the President of the United States. When a child is young, the mind is free. The cells are open and ready to transform whatever is taught into a second nature, into lasting powers, not ephemeral talents. Some parents know this fact, and decide to *design the destiny* of their child.

Yet this concept is *dangerous*, like a *deadly hawk* hurtling down upon its prey, eyes focused and wings closed like scissors.

There is an ancient adage that says: "The fathers shall eat rotten apples, and the sons' teeth ... will get *dark.*"

Standing on my roof with a hot cup of tea, I watched as the steam swirled high. On the street, I saw a little child. Though he was screaming and mentally stressed ... he could still *effortlessly* speak in his mother's tongue.

That moment encapsulated the greatest complaint of ... "For how long must I practice this talent?! ... Can't this power just be mine like my mother's tongue – *A SECOND NATURE?*"

Second natures are lasting powers, unlike ephemeral talents that need to be practiced daily and can be ruined by even the slightest mental stress. Second natures, rather, are like breathing; they are ingrained in one's being.

Today, there are many athletes whom the world once praised for their innate, indestructible talent. Yet a little mental stress came along, and their talent disappeared, along with their streak of successes. So I wrote on my parchment ...

How can a human being have numerous Second Natures?

There are things that are hidden because of their great power and depth ...
*And with the adventure to discover **the Equation**, the answer shall be found.*

68

No IQ

*It is not a game where the guy with the 160 IQ
beats the guy with the 130 IQ. Once you have
ordinary intelligence, what you need is the temperament
to control your urges that get
other people into trouble.*
– WARREN BUFFETT

When the lords of *The Intellect System* saw that luck and talent had died, they decided to establish their dynasty with 3 children: Logic, Reason, and Common Sense. Together, they were a family whose tagline was … "If you can't convince them … confuse them."

Intelligence is what you use when you don't know what to do.
– JEAN PIAGET

Intellect is like vanity, a great seducer promising success. When one is most convinced that intellect is the answer, that is when one is most under a spell.

Intelligence is power, but the IQ is only an iota of the infinite powers stored within the human mind. Ambition, charisma, perseverance, mental flexibility, mastery of improvisation, bravery, street smarts, and the third eye that reads one's own emotions and the emotions of others … all these powers are far superior to IQ and cannot be measured by any written test.

The results of such tests change as one moves from one mental state to another. A house of cards can be toppled by the breath of a fly.

Of all the human organs … the brain is most likely to experience mutability – the capacity *to transform*. A person can rise one morning with an average IQ … only to spark a revolutionary innovation the next day.

Ironically, IQ implies money. Yet in the markets of the world, what makes money is not the boring products of the intellect, but the excitement of novelty and innovation.
A wise buyer will always say to the young entrepreneur, "Don't show me an intellectual model, I have my own people to do that. *Show me the innovation!*"
Charles Darwin wrote, "I was considered by all my masters and my

father, a *very ordinary boy, rather below the common standard of intellect.*"

Intelligence is a matter of perspective. In Northern parts of the American continent, verbal and mathematical skills are associated with intelligence. However, in seafaring cultures and many island nations, they measure intelligence by spatial memory and the navigational arts.

No human being should delay the future just to receive a stamp of approval such as IQ. The individual is the vital decision maker who determines their own destiny. Enlightened *decisions* come after one **transforms.**

> *When making a decision of minor importance, I have always found it advantageous to consider all pros and cons.*
> *In vital matters, however, such as the choice of profession, the decision should always come from the unconsciousness,*
> ***from somewhere within ourselves.***
> – *SIGMUND FREUD*

Don't Judge by Knowledge or Experience

In my mission to excavate the *Treasure*, I dug ever deeper. Uneaten rice by my side and unkempt hair whirling about my head, I was fatigued. I had unlearned some of the walls blocking my mind, but there were more walls to tear down. For if even one wall remained standing, *The Equation* would be lost … forever hidden in the margins of history.

I turned the knob and opened the door to my roof. Using a little telescope, I motionlessly observed the trees, the breeze on the leaves, the sand and the ants. I dropped stones of different shapes with various velocities. And then I was ready to return to my room … and write.

> ***Logic is a systematic method of coming to the wrong conclusion with confidence.***
> *–MURPHY'S LAW*

In studying history and being a part of life, one discovers that just because something makes sense, it doesn't mean it will work.

For those who care about lifting others up, and for those who care about the profits of ambition … judging people according to

70

their knowledge and experience is equivalent to a vehicle driving in the wrong direction, while the driver is dressed for the wrong party.

Experience is simply the name we give to our mistakes.
– OSCAR WILDE

Scrutinizing résumés is a concealed trap. To discover people's true selves and reveal what hidden powers are stored in their minds … one can of course test them by giving them power … or one can wait to discern their mental states in moments of *distress* (but this can take *time*).

Experience and knowledge have zero effect when compared to how a person steers his or her subconscious, revealing what the person believes in.

Both in the world of wealth and in personal relationships, one spends years and precious resources on someone they *do not even know*.

"What good is it to have experience or knowledge if they are not *perpetually* transformed into innovation?" I wrote on the map of my map. Without application, knowledge is pointless – an outdated library.

Imagination is more important than knowledge.
– ALBERT EINSTEIN

Judging people according to knowledge and experience is tantamount to a rich man having no teeth to eat his almonds.

We can see clearly enough that usage is more effective than reason in introducing new things among us and wiping out the old.
– BALDASSARE CASTIGLIONE

The creator of the fairytale with a hero named Skywalker, had no major experience to prove that an upcoming global enterprise was on its way. Out of the garages of a valley rose the information age, helmed by young visionaries with almost no experience to prove anything. Nevertheless, the future was written, and history was made.

When one sees a STAR shining in the sky, should one ask for a résumé?

Judging people according to knowledge and experience mirrors one's own false sense; it reflects the judge's own short sightedness and fear of taking risks. It is easy to see the obvious, but it takes greatness to see *the future* that lies beneath the surface.

Instincts lead ... logic does but follow.
– WILLIAM JAMES

One can be 70 years old with all the experience and knowledge ... yet have no emotional intelligence whatsoever. Inversely, there could be a 15- year-old boy ... who can read the jokes on bubblegum wrappers and know how to transform the world forever. As the saying goes: "He who comprehends what has been destroyed, has better experience and understanding than he who holds the ruins."

In 1783, the hero who crossed the Delaware addressed a group of Irish immigrants with a field of *dreams* ... "Gentlemen, ... the bosom of America is open to receive not only the opulent and respectable stranger, but the oppressed and persecuted of all nations ...; whom we shall welcome to a participation of all our rights and privileges, *if by decency and propriety of conduct they appear to merit the enjoyment.*" And in the words of Marcus Aurelius ...

Whenever you meet someone, ask yourself FIRST this immediate question: what beliefs does this person hold?

Don't Judge by Character First

As the darkness wore on ... one night, I stood on my roof studying the stars on a scroll. Without warning, a little bird flew by me and banged its head against the glass window. Falling to the marble floor, the bird struggled for its life. I tried to revive the bird with water but decided not to touch its body for fear of breaking one of its tiny bones. The next morning the bird had died ... and all the flies were celebrating.

The Vikings first visited the shores of what would become the United States of America, though

it was Columbus who subsequently
demonstrated the politicians
*art ... **of arriving late***
but claiming all
the credit.

Character ... Oh! Character. The very precious stone from which one carves the future. Though history proves again and again, that when one is judged by character first ... the results can be catastrophic.

What upsets people is not things themselves
but their judgment about the things.
– *EPICTETUS*

"The least likely" is a story that has repeated itself throughout history. Those individuals who were "the least likely" to be someone, ended up at the top. A tennis player named Stan was denied as a ball boy for a championship match because he was "too awkward and clumsy" in his character. (He eventually went on to win this championship cup).

A historic king, regarded by his family as a black sheep, a youth of no exalted character. This lad ... whose name now signifies timeless poems ... went on to forge a princely empire, leaving archeological trails.

Judging people by character first is equivalent to running on a machine for 30 minutes and then thinking one can run the same distance on the street during a hot day. The foam of a drink is an *optical illusion*; it leaves one guessing how much liquid is actually there.

A blocked mind is short sighted – seeing through a tube where the opening gets smaller and smaller ... somewhat blinded to characters. Inevitably, judging by character first leads one to step into the trap of beauty. The masterpiece, *The Picture of Dorian Gray*, proves how people become blind when beauty and charisma sweep the streets; everyone is drawn to these powers as a man is drawn to a Greek Siren.

The 29th President of the United States rose to the top because of his good looks and charisma. Everyone was hypnotized ... only to write on the pages of history ... about the disappointments.

73

Charisma is a cosmic weapon of widespread annihilation.

Evil rulers reshaped reality because, in the beginning, people were mesmerized by their electrifying charisma – a mystical escape from the boredom of the mundane.

So the riddle of judgment remains a choice …

> *Bored, midnight … The phone rings.* **Temptation.**
> *Where shall you go?*

The hands of the clock had measured several weeks since I had begun the journey to discover *Time's Silent Secret: The Equation.*

"I can see better now," I said to myself after tearing down the walls that had blocked my mind. "Now the map will show more clues…"

A grand gallery of books glittered before me; *Mathematical Principles of the Natural World, The Harmony of the World, I and Thou, The Structure of Scientific Revolutions, The Revolution of Heavenly Spheres…*

I began to feel weirdly tired. Everything around me seemed to be quiet, suspended in silence. It was as though flying bullets were passing by me … and I was watching them move in slow motion.

My mother sensed severe strain wearing on me and said, "Just remember, Son, for every Promethean triumph … there is a Pandora's box of punishment." I rolled up my sleeves. I ascended to my room … and entered the kingdom of the pen.

The 4 Ds – Decisions, Determination, Dreams, Destiny

When a human being is born … a seed of destiny is planted. The very first breath the baby takes begins to awaken this seed contained within.

Imagine the sun and all the planets orbiting it. Each planet is a human with a unique color and a seed of destiny, a gravitational force that binds the human to orbit life through a certain trajectory … And right there was a clue to *The Equation.*

Every human being was endowed with the unalienable right to make ***decisions***.

74

So what happens when one decides to break this gravity? To transform the trajectory of destiny? To write a new future for oneself? Thinking in my room, I wrote, "Expansion of character … is connected to expansion of destiny."

Character is Destiny
– HERACLITUS

Only what we have wrought into our character during life, can we take away with us.
– WILHELM VON HUMBOLDT

Actions are the seed of fate; deeds grow into destiny.
– HARRY S. TRUMAN

Just as the painter paints on *the plain* canvas, transforming it into a multicolored work, and the sculptor carves the stone into its destiny as a statue, so does carving and expanding one's character change one's destiny. But right then a question surfaced. *How does one carve character and design destiny?*

As I looked over the events of history and the lives of great human beings … the answer wasn't positive thinking or habits. If one thinks positively all day long, will one have the characteristics of Isaac Newton or Adam Smith?

Thinking positively and establishing good habits are important, but they are just tools. They cut the trunk of the tree, but don't cure the roots. So the riddle remained…

How does one carve the character and design destiny?

Then I saw a line by Napoleon Hill: "The reason why man may become the master of his own destiny is because he has the power to influence his own subconscious mind." To steer the subconscious is a mystical art; a great part of it is picking up the right archetype; carving from the subconscious a super-self … expanding the character.

But how does one do that? How does one open the all-knowing eye to connect character with destiny?

Then suddenly, the flame of my candle went out. I rekindled it … and its light drew my eyes to a line in a near-by book.

History will be kind to me ... for I intend to write it.

The line echoed ...

History will be kind to me ... for I intend to write it.
– WINSTON CHURCHILL

Midnight.
Alone on my roof, I watched a curtain of clouds covering the moon.
Then the clouds altered their will and their trajectory shifted a
different way. The moonlight illuminated the darkness of the night
... and then through the passageway, I ran to the hall of records.

Flipping through ancient books, I discovered a secret
proverb ...

Make your will his will ... and his will your will.

When one has a new dream, one enacts a new will ... a
determination that is not on the Universe's schedule. The Universe
is busy with other things on its agenda, very much like a parent or a
buyer.

So if one decides to alter the trajectory of destiny, to expand
destiny with new dreams and wills ... how does one make his or her
new will the Universe's will?

NEGOTIATIONS.

Robert Kennedy said: "Only those who dare to fail greatly can
achieve greatly." This modern remark is united with an old story:
the story of Abraham and the cities of Sodom and Gomorrah.

Abraham *decided* to break with the prescribed future and design
a new destiny by *negotiating* with The Creator. Abraham took a risk
and challenged the Creator, asking that the evil cities be saved on
the merit of a few good men who might be found there.

Another universal story, the story of Noah and his ark, reveals *a
message* of how an individual has the power to design destiny. And
The Creator said: "I will blot out man whom I created from the face
of the earth, from man to animal, to creeping things and the birds of
the sky, for I regret I created them."

Unlike Abraham or Moses, Noah decided to accept the future
and not design a new destiny for his generation, who was washed
away by a flood.

76

After the flood, when Noah saw the extent of the destruction, he only then questioned The Creator about how such a thing could have happened. The Creator replied a *timeless message*: "You are a foolish shepherd. Now you say this! Why didn't you say this when I told you that I saw your righteousness among your generation, or later when I said that I would bring a flood upon the people, or later when I said you should build an ark?! I constantly delayed and wondered, 'When is this Noah going to ask for the compassion of the world?'"

When one decides to write a new future, one should carve the subconscious like a stone, picking up one or more mystical archetypes – to create a super- self ... to expand the character.

Expanding the character means expanding destiny. And by having inner negotiations within one's own mind – making one's new will, the will of the Universe's – one discovers how to design a new destiny according to the times and the character one chooses.

The Future isn't a gift, but an achievement.
– JFK

Destiny is not a matter of chance, it is a matter of choice, it is not a thing to be waited for, it is a thing to be achieved.
– WILLIAM JENNINGS BRYAN

A young man named Ronald designed a first layer destiny of becoming an actor, then a second layer destiny of becoming a Governor, and then a third layer destiny of becoming the President of the United States of America.

Each human being has empty vessels – empty layers of destiny waiting to be designed by the individual. When a layer is fully designed, when the vessel reaches its ***maximum energy*** – the vessel explodes, and the destiny is achieved.

But the question is ... how does one get the cosmic energy to accomplish it all? For the bigger the action, the more energy is needed.

Suddenly, the candle's flame went out again. My room seemed to recede into a *black hole*, and menacing mysteries reverberated ...

How does one get Cosmic Energy?
How does one bring the all-knowing eye to life?

And without having the faintest idea, the *Darkness* whispered …
Hell*o*.

The 4 Ts – Tears, Time, Tragedy, Transformation

The expedition to discover *The Equation* entered a dark ocean
cloaked in mist. Instruments and chalks could not navigate the ship
in this murky zone of intricate knots. The black shroud enveloped
the deck, and I blinked my eyes in hope, following the clues along
with the music of my *nightlight*.

The Buddha, along with other enlightened thinkers through the ages,
followed the courage of their conviction that everything changes
everyday. Not a leaf, a molecule, or a particle of sand is the same
today as yesterday. This clue led the quest forward …

Astronomers with powerful telescopes discovered that the universe
is **EXPANDING** … and the rate of expansion is *accelerating*
because of a mysterious force called **DARK ENERGY**. This force
challenges gravity and bends light.
    The principal substance of Planet Earth is water, but over 95%
of the entire universe is composed of *Dark* Energy and *Dark* Matter.

This clue navigated the *vessel* …

Then I discovered that certain *dangerous dark* animals, such as
brightly colored frogs, eject from their *deadly* skin, chemicals that
create medicine. "Could it be that *evil dark* poison can be a force of
light?" I wrote on the parchment.

The map revealed a gate…

The dog, humankind's most loved animal, a beacon of *light* … has
evolved from the creature mankind fears the most – *the wolf*.
    The wolf is commonly considered a cold, *evil*, *dark* animal,
symbolizing the threat of death … yet in the Greek language, the
word for wolf is *lykos*, which is related to the Latin word for light –
Lux.

The ship to discover *The Equation* sailed through a tunnel …

78

bending the walls of space, guiding me to a secret corner of the Vatican Museum.

A feeling of a stampede ... I fell to my knees and ***the tears*** poured from my eyes as I beheld Rafael's treasure – *The Transfiguration.*

"Where were you? I was looking all over for you," my mother said, flustered. Still in awe, I slowly lifted my head up and told her ... "I found the lost key."

Roll the Rose

One complains about the jacket that needs to be carried
on a hot day ... can't one see that this jacket
is a gift when the night turns cold?

The source of Cosmic Energy in a human being, the key for ***Transformation*** and the awakening of the all-knowing eye ... is a ***Tragedy***.

To be worn out ... is to be renewed.
– LAO TZU

Children scream and shout and *suffer* because new teeth are emerging.

A young prince from Egypt saw a bush that had to be *burned with fire* before enlightenment could sweep his mind.

On the of pathway up to success, one must climb the *thorns* of the rose, only then can one breathe the rarefied air of the zenith.

Inevitable tragedy brought by the Universe is the switch that triggers the hidden powers in the mind, pouring cosmic energy into one's body, and making one young again ... so as to pick up more second natures; lasting powers.

The components of DNA spell ...

TCAG

After playing with these letters as a chemist would a concoction ... I happened upon a silent secret.

TCAG = **T**ransformation **C**omes **A**fter tra**G**edy. (The *4th* letter...)

From the *horrific* war between the North and the South … a **tragedy** that killed thousands, a *good decision* emerged, and the Emancipation Proclamation freed many people.

Egypt is known today, because Britain's greatest sailor *bombarded and utterly* destroyed the French fleet that was anchored off the Egyptian shore.

The Crescent suffered the *unspeakable horrors* of the Mongols, only for the Mongols to later *transform* into great patrons of the Crescent's art.

The same Roman Empire that prosecuted 12 followers would be the one to *transform* and spread news of the Cross.

The wall that *tragically* divided The East and West of Berlin, would *unite* two countries that were at war not long before.

Beethoven had to suffer the *tragedy* of becoming deaf, only to *transform* and create his astounding heavenly music.

Louis Braille lost his eyesight at the age of 3, only to *transform* and invent a reading system for the blind.

Helen Keller suffered the *tragedies* of being deaf and blind, only to inspire the world.

The magnum opus – *Paradise Lost* was written 16 years after Mr. Milton lost his eyesight.

Joan of Arc *tragically* suffered, only to *transform* and lead her country.

Prince Siddhartha went through *hellish* meditations before he transformed and attained enlightenment.

A young Arab prince born in Mecca became an orphan at an early age and later lost his beloved wife … only to transform and change the world forever.

The stars send tragedies to those they love,
So that they shall pick themselves up and transform.
and through their new energy and innovations …
can humankind reach the stars.

The Codes in Numbers

The journey to discover *The Equation* was in the middle of its 6th month. Though the trials of the mind had worn me out, the compass's needle started to point to the end of the *dark* tunnel, leading to the *light*.

History is more than the path left by the past; it shapes the future for it is the union of letters and numbers.

I decided to unlock the gates to the empire of numbers, for numbers have 2 meanings: the scientific and the cosmic … this led me to search for hidden codes in Numerology and Gematria.

Sheaves of documents on Geometry, Chemistry, Math, and Quantum Physics mingled on the table with Pascal's Triangle, Gauss's Bell Curve, Euclid's Elements, and the works of Nicomachus.

As a child paints in kindergarten, my notebooks were painted with the circles of Copernicus and the periodic table of elements.

The moon emerged from behind the clouds, and the night brought a cold wind.

I went to my window. I exhaled hot breath on the glass, and with my finger I traced various combinations of numbers.

Codes, digits, and information ran across the screen of my mind. Then the speed reduced to slow motion, and I picked up 2 numbers.

4

· *4 parts of the day: Night, Morning, Afternoon, Evening*
· *4 basic states of matter: Liquid, Gas, Plasma, Solid*
· *4 regions of Planet Earth: North, South, East, West*
· *4 symbolizes the Mandala and the Tree of Life*
· *4 Elements: Fire, Water, Earth, Air*
· *The human heart has 4 chambers*
· *4 seasons of the year*
· *4 wisdom teeth*

2

· *2 symbolizes division and union: Life & Death, Day & Night, Left & Right*
· *2 is the atomic number of Helium (destined to fly)*
· *2 is the first magic number in physics*
· *2 legs allow humans to save energy*
· *2 is the first plural number*

The Dream

My mind was vibrating. I had no clue how to unite the numbers and the forces into *the Equation*. A disheveled state, piles of papers, sleepless nights, and burned candle wicks, had lurched my sensory system with nerves.

Pacing back and forth in my room, I thought, "Leaving for the desert is not the answer … treasures are always discovered within." Then my sight landed on the magnificent green field across from my house. Its mysticism had inspired me since the very first day I saw it.

"But I need some form of action that will dig out *The Equation* from the margins of history. What can I do?" I wondered.

As a warrior paints his face before going into battle, as a lizard changes its colors, and as Dante was guided by Beatrice … A long time ago I asked a wise alchemist, "What is the one thing you do before making a *decision*?"

The alchemist smiled and said, "That is easy, I go to my wife's chamber … and put her lip-stick on." *Emotional intelligence.*

The echoes of the past inspired me. "Let's take it literally …" I found a *rose*-colored lipstick. I took off my shirt and drew on my body a triangle, a circle, a square, a leaf, a line, the symbol of Libra, a star, numbers, letters, a pentagon, and the symbol of infinity.

With an audio system, a pen, a blank parchment, and a little table, I descended to the arena of the green field.

The night was bright when I opened an envelope my mother had given me at the inception of my journey; on it was written a single line …

whatever is hidden … is within all living things

The wind rushed through my hair, the grass rippled around my feet, and I turned on a song like a prayer.

For 2 hours, I danced to the beat of the song … to break the mists of time, to *free the mind!*

When the sounds started to fade away along with the energies of my body, the page was left blank. I could not see *The Equation*. I fell to my knees in despair and shouted to the heavens: "What more do I need to do?!"

Panting, I whispered, "Help me … don't leave me."

An angelic like wind swept the green field, and my eyes followed a little leaf that soared up and away, revealing a falling star in the

84

night sky above. My eye shed a lonely *tear*. I laid my head on the grass ... and fell asleep.

That night ... What a night ... As a telescope reveals secrets of the Universe's past to the astronomer, my subconscious led my eyes to see a vivid dream.

A time dimension full of bright colors in the shape of a cable.
A channel – the feeling of a satellite orbiting the Earth –
transported me to see hidden secrets of history.
In a split second, the time dimension dropped me, leaving me
hovering in the sky. Looking around, I saw nothing but
bright skies and clouds blinking on and off, covering the rays of the
sun. Below me I saw a garden. To the left I saw a tree, its trunk in
the shape of a double helix, its apples half green and half red.
Beside the tree stood a young Isaac Newton,
his long jacket blowing in the wind. Suddenly his left eye shed a
tear.
The tear traced his jaw and fell to the grass.
An apple fell from above.
Young Newton picked it up, turned, and in the sky
saw a crystal cube transforming light into a rainbow.
The time dimension pulled me back into its kaleidoscopic conduit,
and I was transported to a room where everything was black and
white. I saw a columnar bookshelf laden with papers and pamphlets
to the left, And discovered a young Albert Einstein to the right, the
right side of his face pressed into the table in despair...
A tear fell and flew into the air.
It transformed into energy, the eyes of young Einstein lit up and
he went to the blackboard and wrote $E=MC^2$.
A supernova explosion occurred, leaving me in a colossal crater,
surrounded by ancient layers of rock.
The earth started to shake, carving cracks across the crater's walls.
One by one, 4 streams of the 4 elements from the 4 regions
coursed into the crater and whirled together into a tornado.
Then, from its center, in gold ...

I woke up – the treasure had been discovered.
Sitting on the green field, awe paralyzed my body. I stormed to the table. I picked up the pen and inked *Time's Silent Secret* on the parchment ...

THE EQUATION
$4 = T^2 D^2$

When an archeologist finds a treasure, it's never just about the treasure, but also about decoding its mysteries.

The dream whispered that *3 Articles* and *4 Rings of Power* are bestowed upon those who hold ***The Equation***, so I decided to write them on the parchment.

Article 1: The Third Law of Newton

T^2 = T multiplied by T

One's consecutive *Transformations* multiplied by one's final *Tears* multiplied by …

D^2 = D multiplied by D

One's consecutive *Decisions* multiplied by one's *Destinies* …

Equals … 4

The relationship between the T^2 and the D^2 is in accordance with the Third Law of Newton: the mutual forces of action and reaction between two bodies are equal and opposite.

If one first decides to achieve one's destiny, or decides to design a new one **(D^2)** … this will activate the **T^2** component, meaning that tragedies will shape reality *accordingly*, so one will be able to transform towards a higher state – and achieve the necessary abilities for the destiny chosen. The same rule, the same force, applies in the opposite direction.

Article 2: There is No Evil

Tragedy tempts one into thinking that evil exists. Nevertheless, the pages of history illustrate that tragedies were the keys to transformation and union. When a brilliant September morning turned into terror, when a dark cloud of distorted science covered Europe, when depression swept the land of Lady Liberty, when natural disasters destroyed the shores of the Earth … Slowly but surely … these tragedies brought people together. Suddenly all their differences were wiped out; all their disagreements looked so petty. *The Equation* proves that evil does not exist as a separate force luring human beings to the dark side.

86

Evil is created only when human beings decide to create it. Every force is a force of light, but one has the freedom to choose whether to see it.

The darkest hour of Night is one with the Dawn.

Article 3: The Tear

One should never wish for tragedies. When they inevitably come, however ... know they are for *transformation*.

Only after the dream did I see that it is not about the tragedies themselves, but about the decision to share one's pain – *to shed tears*.

Many people suffer the burns of indescribable tragedies, and yet they decide not to write their own future.

When a tragedy attacks and one decides to shed tears ... these *tears* are an internal restart, resetting the inner system and breaking down the walls of the mind ... In a way ... one attends one's own funeral.

As one cries, time lapses, and life moves in slow motion. The inner universe starts to shrink and accumulates energy from living things. When this accumulation reaches its peak ... the last tear falls.

This singular tear is the most powerful form of the will. When the tear falls ... life is suspended ... the clock breaks ... the world becomes mute.

If one decides to transform before the tear fades away, transformation is achieved. One second later ... the gift is gone forever.

Upon making the decision to transform, one has 2 choices.

+1. *Powers of Light*
–1. *Powers of Darkness*

No matter the choice ... the *transformation* is a new independence day, a supernova, an inner Big Bang – a *REBIRTH*.

And with it come 4 Rings of Power ...

Ring 1 – Water: The Fountain of Youth

By the lords of wealth and by the poor … youth is desired by all. *The Fountain of Youth* doesn't contain magical liquids that one drinks to appear young again … *Youth* means 3 enlightenments.

The development cells that allow children to learn a language without a master and gain many *second natures* are reactivated.

Second natures are lasting powers beyond ephemeral talents. After one transforms, one can choose the second natures necessary for the chosen destiny. These powers do not need to be practiced.

The second enlightenment of the Fountain of Youth is a mental state that unites opposites in the mind; the capacity to linger between *the Column* and *the Star*.

Providence yet Atoms
Poetry yet Science
Spirituality yet Commerce
Book Smart yet Street Smart
A Warrior's sense of urgency yet a Monk's meditation
Speaking yet Creating

The third enlightenment of *The Fountain of Youth* is *never* forgetting the lessons learned along the way.

A young Corsican prince neglectfully reaped all the crops on the way to destiny. When he needed to travel the same route again … there were no crops, no bread crumbs, no lessons to brighten the way.

It's easy to be successful … but it is worlds harder to remember the lessons and passions of the path one traveled in youth, driven by the desire to reach the top and expand.

Ring 2 – Wind: Telescope Fear

Telescope Fear is not the common fear of: "No, I can't." After one transforms, a new super-consciousness is born – the all-seeing eye.

The decision to design destiny, to reshape reality by influencing the network of energy … requires this third eye to see deep into the streets of the future.

Telescope Fear is a plaintiff's fear; the even judgment necessary to negotiate a new future. *Telescope Fear* is the ability to refrain from being overly confident. A transformed being should not

88

write a new future without seeing the side effects of his or her destiny, for each destiny has side effects.

The destiny of the Palace Versailles was designed for perfection. It was to be an exquisite dream where the mind would go giddy. When it was finished … there was no more room to dream … and people replaced life with illusions.

Telescope Fear is an inner warning, a telescope that guides one to see the aftermath of each wish … many years down the avenue of the stars.

Ring 3 – Earth: The Moment
Pick Up!

The alchemy of the moment is more than the power of the performer or the gold medal of the athlete.

Every single moment contains with it centuries of scientific and creative breakthroughs. These moments are ancient molecules; they're messages floating up from the subconscious; they include those rare moments when an archeologist decides to stop searching … and right then, the treasure is revealed.

After one transforms, one picks up innovations and treasures, just as a child picks up a flower. One's consciousness can discover these innovations while dancing on the end of a needle or diving deep into the murky depths of the subconscious.

Ring 4 – Fire: Cosmic Energy

Cosmic energy is the union of ambition, passion, enthusiasm, and hard work. The union is something more than the shining sun … it encompasses Economics of Ecstasy.

An adrenaline rush, a glowing thrill, a dicey and ecstatic competition: all are emotions proven by history to be worth more than gold. Profits are made off of these desired emotions – for it is never about the results of the dice … but about the ecstasy of watching them rolling.

These extreme emotions should not be manufactured; they ought to form naturally within and be channeled towards positive prospects. After one transforms … this sense of peaceful ecstasy … envelops one's *fulfilled life*.

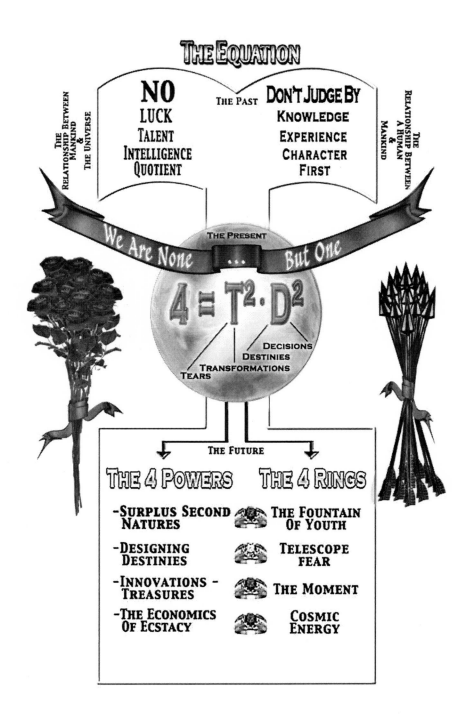

THE EQUATION

NO
LUCK
TALENT
INTELLIGENCE
QUOTIENT

THE PAST

DON'T JUDGE BY
KNOWLEDGE
EXPERIENCE
CHARACTER
FIRST

THE RELATIONSHIP BETWEEN MANKIND & THE UNIVERSE

THE RELATIONSHIP BETWEEN A HUMAN & MANKIND

We Are None ... But One

THE PRESENT

$$4 \equiv T^2 \cdot D^2$$

DECISIONS
DESTINIES
TRANSFORMATIONS
TEARS

THE FUTURE

THE 4 POWERS

- SURPLUS SECOND NATURES
- DESIGNING DESTINIES
- INNOVATIONS – TREASURES
- THE ECONOMICS OF ECSTACY

THE 4 RINGS

THE FOUNTAIN OF YOUTH

TELESCOPE FEAR

THE MOMENT

COSMIC ENERGY

CHAPTER 16
The Day after Destiny

I rolled up the parchment, bid farewell to the green field, and ran to the castle, my feet a speeding turbine. All my energies were tuned to *another* frequency.

It was long after midnight when I opened the gate and ascended the spiral staircase to the parlor.

Panting, I stood there, doubled over, looking at the marble floor. My mother rose from the sofa and said:

"You have aged, my son."

"Mother … may I please have water … I am thirsty."

I hurried past the parlor to the art room. I waited there, and my mother soon rushed in with 2 ice-cold cotton balls and a glass of water.

"Please sit, Mother …" I pleaded as I placed the 2 cool cottons on my eyes.

"I need you to see something."

2 hours past … and Miriam fell back in her chair, her face pale. "My light … what have you done?"

"What do you mean, Mother?"

"This … this … is too …" Miriam mumbled.

"Are you proud of me, Mother?" A child searched for love.

"Yes … but … this is too powerful," she exclaimed.

"I saw *The Equation* in a dream, Mother." I explained the happenings of the night. Miriam remained wary. "If this power were to fall into the wrong hands … like an atomic energy, it would be a chain reaction of darkness."

"But it is for good, Mother. So that people will have a shot in life."

Time crept by for several seconds, and then Miriam uttered potent words: "This is not the right time. It is better if it's hidden."

It felt as though my heart had been ripped open.

"What? I worked on it for 6 months!"

"At least for now … nobody can know about it. Even if you were to show it, son, would anyone believe that a 16-year-old boy came up with it?"

Sadness shrunk me into tears, and I murmured, "But … I …"

"Not now, my light … not now. Every innovation has its time. One day, I promise you, the Equation will be alive." She hugged me close.

"Do you think I will be accepted to an Ivy League School, Mother?"

"Well … I do hope so."

In a sense, archeology is a destructive science. For if one finds an ancient scroll and tries to unfurl it … there is a risk that the scroll will be ruined.

And just when I thought that a Promethean discovery could be made without the side effects of Pandora's box … a collector came to present a bill.

The mind reversed the engineering of time … and a lad started to think he was an old man … not from fear of death, but from a sense that an old soul had taken over, leaving no room for youth.

This opened a heavy mahogany door: competition. Every day the boy would ask everyone around him, "Who is the best? Who is the bravest? Who is the smartest sage? How would you rank them?" Charts and diagrams filled the lad's notebooks as he ranked every aspect of life.

A sense of urgency emerged within him. Every failure added fuel to the fire; he sought out harder challenges; competing with greater fervor.

As embers glowed in the fireplace, the lad would do the same action over and over again, reading the same passage for days, hearing the same song for hours. And when everything was quiet … it started all over again.

One night, the lad sat in front of the music box after hearing its music all day long.

He felt a motherly touch upon his head, as Miriam said, "That's enough, my light. Come … let's *transform* a disadvantage into an advantage."

With love and compassion, his mother mended the imbalance in only a minute. She led him through spiritual exercises, such as finding an object with his eyes closed. Miriam wove self-discipline into the lad's spirit, along with 4 enlightenments …

Genius versus Madman
A genius is someone who does the same action over and over again
…
for a known destiny.
A madman is someone who does the same action over and over
again …
for an unknown destiny.

Beyond Perseverance
Champion athletes and scientists have to do the same action
over and over again, for this is the mental state of perseverance.
Yet self-discipline is the mental state of *refraining* over and over
again from certain harmful actions …

Boring is Beautiful
Doing the same action over and over again is boring.
So why do all of the world's icons convey their messages
over and over again?

The Broken Record of Ideals
Freedom and love are common ideals shared by people.
They are perpetually practiced and perfected, for a brighter future.

When one decides to achieve the future, reality will be reshaped, and a series of tragedies will hinder the way. But if one chooses transformation, the Universe will send a series of presents.

After translating the hurdles into light … the Peter Pan in me smiled again, and I flew through the corridors of the castle, living in peace with the old man within.

All my childhood dreams and heroes sailed to visit me: Britannia, Marianne, Lady Liberty, Prince Siddhartha, my flags and my coats of arms. "G'night, my light," my mother wished me every night as I went to sleep covered in blankets emblazoned with symbols. Nodding off, I would gaze at a painting of a heroic man crossing the Delaware and take comfort in the melody of my music box.

My roof found me immersed in a new a love for words. Day and night I would recite the lines of great leaders celebrating heroism, yet lamenting sorrows.

"Son, from dawn to sunset, you make the roof into a parliament. Take a break."

"A break from what, Father?" I replied. "This is what I love to do. Do you see people taking a break from breathing?"

On one day, I asked my mother if I could get a tattoo, but she said that if I got one, I'd have to leave the house. Upon hearing this, David jumped to his feet and seized the fortune: "Son, let's go and get you a tattoo … I am paying." And the family laughed…

CHAPTER 17
El Dorado

My dream of studying at an Ivy League school was 4 years old, as I navigated the third stage of my schooling.

The ice-cold waters surrounding the finishing school were stark black. Every break left me without a friend. As a special treat … some students in my class would color themselves black on the holiday of costumes.

Finish Line Finesse

Though as a child, I had always hoped for the rainbow to deliver one true friend … I decided to attain a second nature, the lasting power to have no mental trouble with being absolutely alone. If one day I was thrown into the desert for 20 years, my mind would be well-adapted to being alone and having no materialistic needs.

The Ring of Telescope Fear warned my intuition that at some point in the future, I would be alone for many years.

So, by observing the future and being alert to the network of energy, I could start to carve my character correctly, by picking up the right second natures.

"It is never about working 16 hours a day, 7 days a week," I wrote on the parchment. "The winner of the future … is the one who *decides* to sacrifice the *little things* the moment calls for."

It is not how many hours one works … but how one uses the mind. One single moment of a truly transcendent state of mind – in which the all–seeing eye can foresee the future effects of *each decision* – is tantamount to one full month of myopic work. These negligible decisions in this evolved state of mind are what reshape reality, spark magic, and cause one to cross the finish line of one's future … with finesse.

The Champagne of Chic

Different bodies like different things. Vehicles like oils, the human body likes sleep, and the earth likes water.

"The question is …" I scribbled in the sand next to my house. "What does the physical world like? What does the non-transformed mind desire (aside of moderate passion and numbers)?" I drew the answer on the sand …

Charisma

My philosophical quest to uncover the concept of cool converged on my style-setter uncle … Ronin Beatty.

To a 17-year-old lad who was interested in esoteric treasures, Mr. Beatty surprisingly advised, "You can know all these Aristotle things, but if your endeavors have no effortless chic … you are going to encounter difficulty."

Ultra popular at the time and with high-caliber athleticism, Ronin would speak of the art of wearing a suit, how to spray cognac-colored cologne, how to elegantly position the sunglasses and the importance of rapport.

Mr. Beatty would pick me up in his vehicle, adorned with the symbol of a rearing horse, and we would drive to concert halls with neon lights.

Splashes of water would hit my face as the car moved like a speeding meteor and the cool air brought goose bumps to my skin. *Competition* was the propelling force behind our rapport, very much like in the markets of the world. Our competitive temperaments would meet head-on, and I lost in every game we played together. I assured my uncle, "One day, Ronin, I will beat you."

When the going gets tough … the tough get going.

"If competitive challenge is what excites people to move forward … why do they often choose the easiest challenges?" Miriam pondered aloud.

"It is easy to reach the top by using all the means necessary to ruin strangers on the way. *It is easy to become bitter after a tragedy.* It is easy for artists to delve into the subconscious and mix all they find without caring about the dark effects."

Many nights, while listening to the melody of my music box, I would lay there … longing for achievement. Miriam would ascend to my little room, saying, "El Dorado, my light. El Dorado … The lost city of gold is a mystical code for the human to look within and find golden knowledge … the knowledge that triumphant competitors, are those who choose the toughest challenges."

PART 2
WANDER

CHAPTER 18

Station I – Spain

The magical spell of the Ivy League school continued to captivate me. For over 5 years ... I had thought that those historic dorms and libraries would be the ladder to my future.
There is no doubt ... the mind is not without a sense of irony.

David was aware of my aspiration and presented a complication.

My father began to firmly speak of the day when his eldest son would take the helm of the family's enterprise. While David believed in nepotism, it wasn't my cup of tea – and I instead told him the story of Jean Baptiste Bernadotte and other similar tales. A most persuasive argument rose from David's lips, "Plans and profits end when Hades collects the last check. I will always support you, but believe it or not, going to school is like having a Plan B; one relies on the undertaker's wrench, an illusionary shortcut to a Plan A."

Suddenly, golden coins and silver bills glimmered in my mind, luring me to *intellectually* think, "Look how much *luck* you have. It makes sense; your life will be cushioned by a plush chair. Don't walk into the unknown."

I didn't know who I was or what my future held, but as I looked at the stars, my heart chose a different path ... something unknown, yet hopeful.

One day, David played his ace card. "Son, many children leave their homes just to avoid seeing their family. But you? Unconditional love was bestowed upon you since you were born."

Though there is no life without sacrifice, *the tears* for lost moments with my family ... shall follow me like my shadow.

The third stage of my schooling drew to a close. The delicious smell of freedom was wafting in the air ... inspiring me to jump on trampolines and not attend the commencement ceremony.

I was transported by the moment. A newfound sense of independence led me to seek my future. But soon this bright light was blurred in a dust bowl.

"Should I join to the order of the army?" I pondered, as I sat on my roof in the stillness of twilight.

An epic battle of *opposing* powers ensued. "On the one hand," I wrote, "Many of my heroes are generals. On the other hand, when will peace replace the disorder of war? ..."

The dusk casted reddish illumination on a book which laid open on my lap: Don Quixote. Suddenly the wind urged me to descend from the highest point of the roof to the railings.

There, far away in the green field, I saw my mother's scarf billowing in the breeze. "How does she do that?" I asked myself.

I descended further to the green field and found 4 black stones arranged in a line; behind them laid 4 books.

"Please sit down, my light." Seated behind the books, Miriam spoke to me lovingly. "How much you have grown, young one. I can see the fear you are facing, but I can only give you wings ... you are the one who must fly. I can present you with the stones, but you are the one to choose."

"Do you want me to pick up a stone?" I asked.

"Yes ..."

"What are these stones?"

"Under each stone is a paper inscribed with the name of a city. So close your eyes, connect to your inner light, and beneath your chosen stone you shall discover the clue."

I closed my eyes, straightened my spine, structured my body in a meditative pose, and pointed to the fourth stone, farthest to the right.

Miriam turned the stone over. I picked up the note, and my mother handed me a book ... *Napoleon Bonaparte.*

"Be prepared," Miriam said. "You are going to Spain."

5 days before the adventure, the stars pointed to the expeditions of Columbus and the romance between Queen Isabella and Ferdinand. On the day of my departure, a Spanish guitar played as the engine of the plane roared to life ... and the magical stallion soared up and away.

I landed in Barcelona to the smell of the Mediterranean breeze and the sights of a historic city.

My expedition to discover an answer to my military riddle was perceived as a strange separation of sight and sound: while my eyes saw the city, my ears listened to the subtext of the book my mother had given me.

Barcelona was a city rich in art – a creative Mecca – in which Spanish and Catalan mingled into a melody of vibrant voices. The pavilion presented warm-hearted local men and women dressed up in authentic style.

The ancient Greek games unveiled their glory in a stadium, *reminding* me that it was not simply about: "You lose, I win." Instead, it was the dream of the *winning* team awarding the *failed* team.

A lamp flickered on the terrace of my lodge that night. As I read the book my mother had given me, I wrote, "The Rosetta Stone Napoleon discovered interpreted the secrets of Egypt; maybe this book can interpret the riddle of the gap between military heroism and the discord of war."

The speed of my Spanish expedition *accelerated.*

On the way to the city's commerce center, I saw human castles: people in exotic attire were climbing on top of one another to create intricate shapes. I whispered, "If only these human castles had the *accelerated expansion* of commerce … Oh! What wonders this world would create."

The sun was setting behind Columbus's statue, and I returned to my humble abode.

As I sat on the terrace overlooking the city, my military mystery remained unsolved. "Why am I reading a book about the Corsican prince?" I asked the night. "I already *remember* the pages of this historic period."

The days shifted into hyper-speed.

I was lost, wandering through the streets. Then, I heard a cacophony of off-beat sounds, and I followed them and navigated through the crowd. From the ashes of confusion rose a Gothic cathedral. Its sheer magnitude seemed to bend space with surrealism.

As I sat there to read the book, everything started to spin around me like a tarantella. The streets erupted with guitars, Flamenco dancers, and cheerful chatters. Swishing dresses, glittery burgundy, peoples' passions, and the smell of delicious tapas …all broke my concentration.

100

When the city finally fell asleep, I sneaked out of my lodge and returned to the Gothic cathedral. The night sung mystical music, as I found a bright corner and flipped through the pages of my book.

After reading about Napoleon's summit of success and his relationship with the czar... I thought, "Enough. Doesn't reading about something I remember do nothing but waste *time*?"

Right then, a little wind flipped the page ... revealing a new chapter. I began to read about the guerrilla warfare between the Spanish forces and the Corsican prince. The massacre, the butchery, and the horror caused a moral rage to roar through me.

I closed the book and looked up at the full moon ... and the next day, the magical stallion came to fly me home.

The adventure to Spain solved my military riddle by pointing to the North Star.

Becoming embroiled in the disorder of war was not in my heart. And I had a feeling that my future would be written far away ... on the other side of the world.

The Ring of *the Fountain of Youth* endowed by **The Equation**, empowers one to never forget the lessons one learns along the way...

Conquer Your Mind and You Shall Conquer Destiny!
From Alexander to Augustus, from Constantine to Napoleon...
Transformation had endowed these generals with *The Ring* of *Cosmic Energy*.
El Dorado means to compete for the gold while facing the toughest challenges.
The same *accelerated expansion* – the atomic ambition – that they used to conquer lands ... should be transmuted into light, and channeled to conquer the mind.

Don't Remember to Forget
If I knew the Napoleonic history ... why did I forget it?
In art ... though the creator portrays the hero as the one who makes the rightdecision at the end, the reader will likely always remember the rotten apple that was bitten at the beginning,
and claim, "Oh ... I can bite the forbidden apple and reach the top! No punishment will happen to me."

CHAPTER 19
Station II – The Boot

Wandering in the desert of time, and seeking my future in its sands … I was thirsty.

At the age of 13, I had made the decision to study at an Ivy League school. These legendary institutions, with botanic gardens and enchanted halls, cost many golden bills and coins.

"I want to ease the burden on my family's unshaken support," I said, sizing up the matter.

Looking at my dark-skin and my odd looks in the mirror, I felt compelled into proving that success is not about beauty … so I sought to be paid to walk the runway.

Evolving Elements

The magical stallion flew me to the land shaped like the boot. My legs occupied the 2 empty seats beside me as I read *The Odyssey*.

The plane cruised through the city of the clouds, and I wondered, "Who am I? What is my path? Why am I here?"

The Ring of the Fountain of Youth reminded me that each human being sometimes needs to serve before taking the lead, to descend to low valleys in hopes of breathing the fresh air at the mountain's zenith.

A young spiritual leader name John Paul, as well as a young prince named Ronald, were performers as youths. They *picked up* the magical elements of performing and evolved them into a greater destiny. The same success transpires with enterprises … when one innovates.

It was mid winter. My transportation meandered through the cold towards the lodge.

"Excuse me, dear sir," I said to the driver. "Might you know where I can find a panettone cake?"

"But'a o' course…" the driver replied in his thick dialect.

Then the driver inquired where I had arrived from, and when I replied he exclaimed, "Santa Maria! The land of The *Holy Grail*. Me take for the cake if you pray for me family when you get back there, eh?"

"Sir, it will be my honor."

"Y'u know," the driver added, looking in the rear view mirror, "Me

saw your name on luggage. It is'a Rome, if the R put in beginning and voilà. Me teachers say bad in spelling ... ha, I show 'em."
The door swung shut behind me. I held the cake in one hand, and in the other, the suitcase.

The clerk in the lodge's lobby directed me to my little room. "The city has a glamorous nightlife, sir ... would you like a manual?" the clerk offered. "No, I am fine."
And while the clubs of the night flashed their neon lights, a lad sat alone in a room, gazing at the rain.

The grey weather became a bit warmer as I sipped some hot coffee and viewed the statue of the Madonnina the next day.

The city was pricey and required many strange-looking coins. One learns while wandering the desert of life to save a white coin for a black day. So I decided to store my reserves in a jam jar and eat only one meal a day.

3 days went by, and my will to walk on the runway was denied by 5 companies, all concluding, "Strange looks, inexperienced, no presence."

On the way back to the lodge, I crossed Via Monte Napoleone ... History wrote that Prince Siddhartha, the young Corsican and so many others had *transformed* ... and changed their *names*.

Shaking from hunger and fatigue, I ate stale cornflakes at the lodge. A white-haired waiter, radiating with elegance, furnished a fatherly smile. I bowed my head to him and left for the night.

The morning dawned with a chill.
I passed by a building where numbers and securities were traded. I then thought, "The *transformed* mind can alter the exchange of numbers, just as a butterfly in London can influence a hurricane in the Pacific."

7 more companies denied my will to walk the runway. Door after door was sharply shut, and my personnel packages were thrown in the garbage.

And when one representative heard, "Sir, I promise I will project a good example," He started to laugh, saying, "Blasted thing! Who cares about that? In this city you have to sell your soul."

Eating a chocolate bar, I traveled to an antique library. There, I opened a book on the painter of the Mona Lisa and pondered, "How wonderful it is to create innovations that light the future." Then, I flipped through another book, landing upon a page that revealed ...

E=MC². I tore a piece from my parchment, wrote *The Equation* on it, plucked an eyelash, and made a wish … "May it one day be …" I whispered as I placed them both in the book and closed it.

Back at my lodge, the smells of hot fresh food were wafting out into the street from a nearby restaurant. As I was staring through the glass, the chords of poverty played … and I sadly felt the music. I was about to turn away when a little man came out shouting, "Hey you!" He beckoned me over, and I said, "Sir, I didn't mean any harm, I just …"

"You dressed up nice," the chef blurted. "But eyes are sad. I see you hungry. You come eat."

"I do indeed thank you, but I have no means of paying."

"Oh! Dirty things these coins. You hungry, you eat."

On the wall hung a picture of a fighter. "That's my son." The chef was proud. "He is a fighter. Do you know fighting?"

"Well … the only thing I know about fighting is that a famous black fighter refused to enlist in the army."

"Mamma mia!" the chef sped up the second. "I think I know … he shouts all the time he's pretty."

I smiled.

"You alone here. No family. Not easy … come, eat when hungry are you." The chef's short stature paled in comparison to his mammoth heart. I kissed the old man on the cheek, and ascended to my room to sleep.

One grey morning, I ate breakfast at the lodge, viewing the city from an ice-cold window. The still water on the street looked thick like woven cloth, and the ground was covered with frost.

"Excuse me, young man." I felt a hand on my shoulder. I turned to see the waiter I had seen several times before.

"Hello, sir," I greeted.

"Are you by any chance an African Prince?" the waiter asked in his British tongue. I smiled and said, "No sir, I am not."

"Oh, pardon me. There is something about the way you sit. Why do your eyes seem sad, if you don't mind me asking?"

"Well … I want to do good you know, to discover my future."

"My daughter said the same thing," The gentleman replied, his voice weary with emotion. "What does she do, sir?" I inquired gently.

"She was a writer. Every representative rejected her because of her inexperience. Then, one day, one of them promised her the world. She trusted him and was hurt when he took advantage of her."

104

"I am terribly sorry, sir." His story pierced my heart.

"Some time later, my daughter left our home. She never returned … Her mother could not bear the pain and passed away."

"I do feel for you. I also lost someone I dearly loved."

His eyes grew teary, and the man added, "I am still lamenting, you know. I would give away all the money I have for one day with my family." The waiter began to cry, "I apologize, young sir, I shouldn't have troubled you with my tears. It is tough these days to find someone who is willing to listen. I thank you."

My last day in the land of the boot afforded me one final key to walking on the runway, being paid, and opening the gates of an Ivy League School.

I knocked on the representative's door, holding my file. A lady came out, and I said, "My lady, I came from far away, give me a shot. I believe you will not be let down."

The lady scanned my physical body and slammed the door with an earsplitting bang, leaving a bleeding cut on my forehead.

Festoons of holly and mistletoe were hung all over the city. The rain started to pour as I stood all alone on the street.

I left my umbrella behind and wandered into the unknown. The raindrops soaked my neck. I came upon a disheveled old man sitting in a deserted alley.

I gave the meek bearded man all the coins in my pocket and sat next to him for the rest of the night.

CHAPTER 20
Station III – The Eastern Seaboard

"Human beings before me have sailed in stormier seas," I wrote on a piece of paper as the magical stallion entered the kingdom of the skies. "The Universe might have stacked the deck against me, but I shall follow the path to the North Star … In the meantime, I'll continue my past pursuit."

As I turned the final leaf of a book on the adventures of Leif Ericson , the plane landed in a city that kisses the Atlantic Ocean.

The night summoned a black vehicle that drove me to a little lodge. The fresh air had captured my feelings, inspiring me to wander down the sea shore. The smell of fish and my thirst for a fresh drink, reminded me of the days when I grew up like a prince … and now the desire to experience poverty had made life that much harder.

Curiosity led me into an eerie restricted area of a library. "The city was conceived by a woman," a librarian told me tersely as she ushered me out.

I felt like a tribal man carrying his water canteen across the desert. Hope after hope was dismissed, and the days ended in failure.

"I will see someone," I assured myself. I had been waiting outside a building for over 10 hours when a representative appeared, holding a folder.

"Excuse me, sir. I am not looking to bother you. Will you give me a few minutes of your time?"

"Your looks are bad, kid," the man said. "Your passion won't pay for my women."

The breeze of the sea drew me to a dock loaded with cargo. The port protected the ships as they sped in and out.

I stood there – my legs grounded on the harbor, my long jacket billowing in the wind – and scribbled on a small piece of parchment …

Dear Source of Light
Your Grace is golden.
Thy universe is the supreme judge of energy …
Of, by, and for all living things.

106

Let thy torch light the lighthouse that guides my ship,
For the dark flames of the day rupture the armor
of your opportunities.

I folded the parchment and sent it into the waters as a ship's horn sounded its departure in the distance.

Suddenly, out of the corner of my eye, I saw a little card dancing along the ground, like a feather in the air. I picked it up ... and it said that there were tryouts for players on the screen.

"The stage scares me," I thought to myself. "But maybe I am *lucky* to be heading the *wrong* way."

The next day, I went to a street that bordered the ocean. The place bustled with people shouting, screaming, and raising their arms like conductors in front of an orchestra, while a long line of hopeful youths waited under the sun.

A representative approached us and announced with irony, "It's allergy season. We are sensitive to your smell. So obey two rules: one, do as you are told, and two, never lose sight of number 1. Do not leave this zone."

Then, some time later, a lonely butterfly entered the room, zigzagging in the air. It looked like a golden blossom, mingling with the rays of the sun.

I followed it down the stairs, until an old man with slick grayish/white hair spotted me.

"What is your name, young man?" the man asked with his colossal voice.

"I apologize, sir," I responded. "I will go upstairs."

"No, you won't." The man possessed a strong presence. "Who are you?"

Quite perplexed, I replied, "... I don't know."

"How old are you?"

"I am 19, sir."

"19!" the man blurted. "You look like a 35-year-old man. Are you lying to me?"

"No sir. That is my age."

"I see ..." The man's piercing eyes peered at me through his big glasses.

"Maybe I should go upstairs, sir," I swallowed my fear.

"No 'should' or 'could.' And please stop calling me sir. My name is

Paul. You have something; I can't put my finger on it..." Deep in thought he went on: "Take these pages. Come back and read them when you are ready."

I felt the blood drain from my face as I walked to a quiet corner. And right then, when *emergency* consumed me, an *emergence* endowed by *The Ring of The Moment* transpired.

The emergence was called *The Magnet of Hearts*. Imagine a sun that, instead of projecting rays, receives the rays. Each ray is a force, and the sun – the mind – is a magnet.

The Equalizer
Each written sentence is perceived as sound waves.
The ears absorb the frequencies of the lines and channels the tones and the octaves to the mind.
During a performance, the lips spill the music of the words, not lines memorized by rote.

The Flash
One takes mental pictures of lines flashing letters and shapes. As the eyes open and shut like shutters, the mind peeks at the subtext of the written word.

Sensation of Senses
One drinks the lines. One smells the lines like a fresh fragrance.
One touches the lines.

Birds and Verbs
Verbs are a battalion of birds;
they speed in synergy to the mind.

So the riddle remains … which is better?

To speak to the Parliament after studying a speech intellectually, and let the people say, "I get it, but it's so dull."
or
To speak the Parliament after studying a speech creatively, and let the people say, "I didn't get it, but I am on FIRE!"

The rest of my adventure, in the city on the Atlantic Coast, was spent with Paul.

I discovered that Paul was a famous player on the screen. Though a star, his power was not the system, but his soul.

After taking off his hand-knit sweater and giving it to a poor man on the street, he took me for a walk along the coast.

"Finding your future at your age is an almost impossible thing, kid," Paul said. "But you can follow the signs on the way."

"What should I do, Paul?" I asked, fearing the unseen. *"Know Thyself,"* Paul said potently. "I believe in you, kid. Maybe for now you should pursue the path of a performer. Trust me. I have been around the block. *There are no skills*. The best artist is the one who is in *the moment*. Someone who is aware of his or her being." "So what do you say, Paul. Can one be any character?" Paul smiled with wisdom and replied in a low whisper, "No ... when you know who you are ... all characters will bend and become you."

The sunset seemed like an inscription carved in the skies. I stood on the sand before the ocean... and beheld the circle of life.

CHAPTER 21

Station IV – The Desert's Diamond

One has the right to write the future.
More important is the promise to design it ... with light.

Over 6 years ago, a young lad had decided to study in a Legendary School; it was the desperate desire of his heart.

The destinies of a human being are empty vessels within vessels, waiting to be filled by the person so that they may surface to life.

Sometimes ... to forge a more hopeful future, one should unite the destinies, very much like opposing nations sign treaties in order to forge a union, or how enterprises merge to create a conglomerate.

After looking at the future with infrared binoculars ... *The Ring of Telescope Fear* – its *Diamond* – issued an interpretation of the binary codes, "Unite the *decision* to study at an Ivy League School, with the *decision* to summon the archetype of the performer to one's character."

I was wandering in the desert of life with a flashlight, when a lady named Agila appeared. The acclaimed lady embodied the feeling of a magical theater in a forest ... as she pointed me to a master of alchemy.

I opened an old, greyish gate and tried to maneuver through a garden inhabited by toys and indigenous trees.

Within this *monastery of Midas's Stone* ... enchanted by the myth of a touch that *transforms* metals into gold ... a sage said: "The apple will fall ... all these etiquettes ... no use, futile. They try to stretch the meaning of words beyond what is credible, pretending that every step forward is threatened by an impulsive comment or a casual answer."

"What apple?" I asked the old man.

The master picked up his cane and hit the ceiling. An apple that had been hanging by a thin wire fell into my hands.

"You see," the master said. "You didn't need to say, 'good evening, Sir.' "

After he had ricocheted questions, the Midas master, giggling like a child, handed me a parchment, saying, "Your lesson."

110

After withdrawing to the garden and unfolding the parchment, I discovered he had prepared a translated Ancient Greek text for me to read.

The Ring of The Moment – its *Emerald* – endows stimulated reality to the performer, the warrior, and the speaker. With this state of mind, one can achieve *gold* medals.

Imagine, the inner world vibrates, the keys to the subconscious rotate.
Objects outside are engines, sending energy.
The walls of time and space are bending.
The mind is the Universe, liberty.
No beginning and no end.
Action is stillness
One blinks
Rebirth

I went back to the Midas master to perform the lines. He giggled and said, "What a fetching idea!"

The mental state *Between The Column and The Star* is the union of the Physical World (The Column) and the Spiritual World (The Star).

It was time to leave the head in the clouds and go back to root the legs on the ground.

A lady named Mrs. T teamed up with me. She was a chancellor of knowledge about historic campuses. Together we explored every corner of these institutions.

The compass's needle pointed to the island of Britain and then to the 13 colonies, reminding me how I had first decided to design my destiny. Now, nearly 7 years later, I chose 4 legendary schools.

I followed the smell of foul smoke and realized that these legendary institutions like to flick frantically through the pages, looking for *IQ* scores and *experience*.

Opening doors and seeking underground entryways, a member of one of these institutions revealed a secret provision: "The Ivy League outsources courses to other schools."

A plan geared in great speed. "If I go to one of these independent schools, I'll gain the same *experience* of an Ivy League Institution."

Upon hearing my plan, Mrs. T said, "I tell you it is too risky. Giving the tenant the option price to buy the house, so you can own the tenant's parking lot, will require *luck*. These institutions don't like this courage, and even if you do have it … I suggest you spend it on having fun."

The Hero who Crossed The Delaware

Story A becomes Story B when people don't deliver their history.

I carried a large parcel in my hand, and the magical stallion flew me to a school of arts, so I could *independently* deliver my submission.

On the way, I thought about Thomas Jefferson and whispered, "Wherever you may be … happy birthday."

After handing over my history, I wandered to a mystical museum. There I saw, once again, the painting of a hero who, against all the odds, *Designed Destiny*. Like a lighthouse signaling me to the shores of my little future, the painting inspired me to muse, "Who am I? What is my future?"

The Ring of The Fountain of Youth reminded me that the butterfly is the proof that we have a second chance in life; not for nothing… a caterpillar transforms.

I then went to a grand train station, where the horns and tunnels traveled me to Columbus Circle; here I spent the rest of the nocturnal hours.

CHAPTER 22
Station V – 3 Captains Shine the Apple

The lodge was a block away from the school. With its little lobby and a little library on the second floor, the lodge exuded a welcoming spirit.

My room was so tiny that even a needle would have considered the abode a bitsy box.

During the nights, I would scout for secret passages, often encountering a Latin man and an Irish lady who would smile and greet me with grace. During the days, I would face the school with resistance.

Logical research, classes of reason, textbooks of *intellect* ... all just scratch the surface, rarely reaching the core. And when a lad pled with the staff ... well ... they burst laughing, obsessed with bookkeeping.

The headmaster was Mr. Horn. With his hoary beard, well-worn blue outfit, and love of opera, he instructed the students to pick up theatrical pieces to perform.

A *dear* friend chose a *dark* piece. A *sense of urgency* arose in me, and I said, "Energy is energy. The mind and destiny don't know the difference between reality and performance. A dark decision on stage will affect the reality of your future."

7 days later ... his life mirrored the wicked grin of the joker.

U by W
Archetypes exalt human beings ...
while stock characters dehumanize them.

When the pendulum marked my time to perform ... I did poorly. The *failure* fueled the fire to do better, to transcend higher. Back in the lodge, in its little library ... I *decided* it was time to carve my character ... to descend to the murky depths of the subconscious and *pick up* mystical archetypes and colors.

Lighting *The Rings* of *The Moment, The Fountain of Youth,* and *Telescope Fear...* I dove deep into the subconscious.

As the astrologer studies the stars, so should one contemplate their higher self. The higher self is a super character one carves from the subconscious after *transformation* is achieved. Each higher self

113

is a planet. As the Pythagoreans say: "Look at the sky at dawn. Wish to be a planet. A heavenly spiritual body, see their perpetual beauty … they wear no veil."

The subconscious is a vast vault of treasures, innovations, colors, ancient archetypes, and second natures.

After *transformation* is achieved, one has the keys to the subconscious. And with *The Ring* of *Telescope Fear* … one can *design* character in accordance with the future (for if one picks up the wrong archetype … a chain reaction of catastrophes could destroy the mind …).

For the next 4 days, I would enter the grand library of archetypes; The Hermit, The King, The Counselor, The Visionary, The Magician, The Knight – and with the torch of my inner light … *together* we would light the subconscious. The subconscious is in a state of perpetual twilight. Nevertheless, one can carve one's *character* (*U*) *by* uniting *oneself* with *the inner light* (*W*). For if *character* isn't guided *by both*, bad decisions will be made, or one will be lost in the infinite mazes of the subconscious.

At the time … I found it tough to tolerate the suffocating heat of the subconscious, for my *transformation* wasn't complete, and I had *forgotten* to bring *The Ring of Cosmic Energy*.

One midnight, I went down the stairs to the lobby of the lodge. There, sat an old man named Frank. He had blue eyes, brown skin, black hair, and a small nose, and his weight seemed to sink the sofa. "Hi, boy … come here … come to Uncle Frankie," he said drunkenly.

"Hi Frank. How are you sir?" I said noticing his empty bottles of liquor.

"Another day in paradise. Care for a shot?"

"No, sir. I have never had a drink in my life."

"Why are you so serious, boy? I see you! You don't go out, you act like you are older than me. And nobody is older than me!" Frank blasted.

"Frank, would you like me to get you some water or something?"

"Water for what? Who are you to tell me if I need water!"

"Sir, I apologize if I offended you."

I turned to depart …

114

"No … hey! Wait!" Frank shouted. "Come back … come back …"
Breathing heavily and with sad eyes, Frank said, weary with emotion,
"This is a cruel world, kid. I remember when I was your age. Oh … *the dreams* … but I never got my chance."
He downed a shot and went on, "Do you remember what a young prince said in *On The Waterfront*? … 'You don't understand! I could have had class, I could have been a contender … **I could have been somebody!**'
Fight for your future, kid … fight for your future …" The old man closed his eyes. For a split second I thought Frank had passed out … but he had just fallen asleep.

I darted back up to my room and dove again into the subconscious. And an inner sonar discovered *a code*.

The subconscious is like a ship in a crystal bottle. Time doesn't exist there, and there is no beginning and no end.

There are 3 captains who guard the ship; 3 who govern all the mystical archetypes: *The Dreamer*, *The Doer*, and *The Editor*.

No matter which archetype one picks up, one of these captains will touch it … and the archetype shall have that captain's characteristics.

The captains are in infinite war with one another. The greater the dreamer in someone, the less of an editor or doer he or she shall be. The greater the doer in someone, the less of an editor or dreamer … and so on.

After one transforms, one unites the opposites and breaks mental barriers. And all the 3 captains shall shine the apple – one's character.

7 days later, the headmaster, Mr. Horn, confirmed my accolades in a letter so that my dream of studying at an Ivy League School could come to fruition.

One afternoon, near the entrance of the school … I was exchanging words with friends. As I was handing them a parchment entitled *From No to Know,* my heart suddenly shattered like a crystal glass crashing against the floor when, one of the teachers approached me and said, "I'll give you sage advice. Don't waste your time. Soon all this will change; the hope in their eyes will fade … and their dreams will be alone."

For 2 days, I wandered with a flashlight through the forest of life. Retracing the route, I remembered it was my 20th birthday. I was all alone facing the wall in my room, when my eye birthed a *tear*.

What comes after is always in affinity to what went before.

I took a bag, and a train brought me to visit the 4 schools … my will was eager to enter.

Coins became calls, and I would speak with every member who would pick up the line.

A brown-skinned lady, a master teacher of dancing, invited me to her home for dinner and gave me her support. She handed me a parchment inscribed with essential names and numbers, leading me closer to a colonial Ivy.

The next day, the train sounded its whistle and I met a man named Mr. Ponet. His stately cottage had an inscription on the wall: *Urim and Thummim*. 5 days later, the man summoned me again to the bewitching, sweeping lawns of the school. He warmly told me, "I pulled some strings, and I think given your age, you'll be able to address your request directly to the master classes."

Transfixed and overjoyed by *the roulette of fate*, I could now knock on the doors of 5 Ivy League schools. Returning to my lodge in the city, I heard from a member of another school. "I really don't think it's possible to address your admission to both diplomas at once, within the same institution. But let me get back to you," Lady Ader said.

She poured through papers and came back, reckoning with a hypnotic quality, "There is a way …"

The session at the school of the arts drew to a close. 70 days had gone by since I started defying *the fear of failing* my 7-year-long dream of studying in a legendary school. And now I was addressing 6 of them.

Tension was mounting … the battle had begun.

CHAPTER 23
The Olympian Twilight

Machines display a red light to request a restart. The body does the same by becoming tired, but I had *no choice* but to postpone such rest.

To a degree, a human being is a spiritual innovation. One **negotiates** with the Universe, carves his or her character, writes the future, and urges the network of energy (the buyer) to reshape reality.

The buyer represents *silence*; the seller represents *speech*. And just as fire was united with a bush before an Egyptian Prince, so one should unite silence and speech ... in the empire of the mind.

Along with my counselor, Mrs. T, I addressed the 6 Ivy League institutions as the buyer. A library of parchments, letters, and notes was crafted by Mrs. T with the precision of a needle.

Every day, information flashed in, and the schools were bombarded with the same blatant questions ... for the answer of Person A will differ from the answer of Person B.

In a march of conviction, a military general, a doctor, a minister, a lord of wealth, teachers, and masters ... all answered the request of the 6 buyers for transparency ... and wrote letters of reinforcement.

I went to the goblins of the bank. I put *The Wealth of Nations* on the table and said urgently, "Any dream is in danger of a hostile takeover. I need two *poison pills*." The goblin smiled and wrote 2 letters of proof.

"My light," Miriam said. "School will not determine the outcome of your future. Just look at how many great minds dropped out of school or didn't attend at all."

But school screeched like a Greek Siren, and express trains carried large parcels to the 6 schools.

The Eye of The Storm.

> *If one shall die the day after tomorrow ...*
> *Will the prison of time fall before?*

A fleet advanced, undetected by the radar of my mind. One exam left me ablaze with fire. "What is happening to me?" I thought.

That night, after taking a young lady out to dinner, I was driving alone during the late hours of the night. Speeding along a highway … I suddenly fell asleep.

The car crashed against the railings, flipped in the air, and landed on its 4 wheels.

I awoke to a broken nose and the sight of fire blooming from the hood. I hurried out of the car, but remembered that a book of wisdom, written millennia ago by a king, was in one of the compartments. I sprinted back, searched for it, and smuggled it to safety.

In the coming days, the master alchemist – Hill – took me to an amphitheater. Giggling, he said, "This is going to be fun. Remember, forget about time, forget about gravity. *Just be*. Begin!"

The Ring of The Moment created a stimulated reality. I started to read the lines, but anger emerged. My mental state was broken, as the master said, "Again!

The intellect – *the puppeteer* – processed everything again. The mental state fell apart, and the master alchemist led me with wise words: "The intellect leads to confusion, confusion leads to fear, and fear leads to trying. Never try! If no one ever told you that you had limits … how far would your mind reach?"

"Nothing goes well for me. It's *their* fault. Time, life … they stop my future!" I wrote to my mother.

Standing on the roof, Miriam sensed *the tears* of her son. She wrote, "I know how much you love being here, Son. I can only imagine your answer: 'The stars are the only friends I have in the world.' My light … the mind is the creator of your reality. Be in the moment with the Universe." Along with the letter was a little blue box. I continued reading her words: "Close your eyes. Here, I am lifting your hand and slipping this ring onto your *fourth* finger. It is called *The Star of Light*." I could see my mother's hand pointing … "Here is *The Column*, and here is *The Star*. Always embrace this mental state, my son. Unite the physical world and the spiritual world within you."

In the lodge, a friend brought me soup to warm my spirit. I was sitting like a statue, staring at the sky as it poured rain on the planet's soil.

118

The train sped along and stationed a lad at one of the 6 schools. Lady Ader greeted him, saying, "I missed you, but don't expect kindness here. These tryouts pit the professors *versus* the contenders. I wish you *luck*."

The lad's heart did a somersault in the preparation hall. The contest began. He held the ring his mother had given him close to his chest and immersed himself in the lines of the performance.

The next morning broke with another contest. A misty, barren street led the lad to a building. The professor attacked with cold silence, and the lad fought to hold his mental state steady against the onslaught.

The train sped the lad to another frontline. There as a contender, he could feel that the door was shut when a professor hushed with an icy voice,
"Isn't it funny?"
The lad closed the gate behind him.

He walked to the next destination. At the end of the contest, a division of professors approached a wall and hung a notice of congratulations. The lad wished so dearly for his name to be there so that his family and future would be proud. But a sharp-edged realization drained the color from his face. Back to the lodge in the rain, the lad wrote to his mother: "One of the 6 schools fell through. If only I could describe *the tears* of my dream."

On to the next *tear* … "We don't shake hands – *good luck*," a professor said, sipping a tea through pursed lips … appraising *talents*.

I felt as though my insides had turned to ice when I read the next notice on the board. Contenders were scattered like woolen socks, as I turned to see a girl with mulatto skin, curly black hair, and an oval face sitting on on a lonely bench, I asked, "Are you all right?"
In a hoarse voice, she said, *"There is no justice … there is no justice."*

The magical stallion flew above the mists of the Atlantic Ocean … and landed the lad on his roof.

The lad hadn't seen his childhood roof in a long time, and despite its familiar comforts, he could still feel the 100 years of solitude.

2 schools delivered destructive blows and disappeared into the shadows. One morning, after praying for the Italian driver as vowed, the lad encountered the work of a life's trickster.

"Who are you?" a member of one of the schools blurted over the earpiece. "What do you mean, my lady?" the lad asked with fear. "Your name is not in our system." the woman said. "How could that be? I attended the audition and the exam, and I sent a large parcel addressed to your campus."
"Well, I am sorry, young man … *your name is gone.*"

The lad's room had become a bunker. Pale and thin, he watched the window glow with the light of the moon like the eye of a *wolf.* All the while, *the nightlight* played its heavenly melody.

Hermes brought 2 letters. The lad opened the envelopes, and they read: "We regret to inform you …"

With only one more school to hope for, after 7 years of striving, the *tragedy accelerated.* And the lad wandered back to the green field where a dream had revealed *The Equation.*

He knelt on the soil before the sunset of that solstice; the sun seemed to stand still. The lad prayed to The Source of Light. He saw a lemon among the blades of the grass, but he couldn't *transform* it into lemonade.

Back inside, the lad turned the knob of a door. In the parlor, a letter fell from his mother's pale hand. "I am sorry son …"
Time stopped! At that moment the lad's world shattered. He sprinted with passion to the street, *tears* streaming down his cheeks. He reached a black forest late that night. Panting and breathing heavily, he sat in a hidden corner. The world had become mute, and when *the last tear* fell from his eye, the *clock broke* … and a *decision* was made.

Slowly, the lad lifted his head and whispered, "So be it …" He made his way back home, went to his room, wrote his new name on a parchment, and departed to the roof.
There, James took the book he once saved from a burning car and ignited it. The flames blazed before his eyes, and drew him … into the *darkness.*

120

PART 3
THE DARK DAYS

CHAPTER 24
The Sun Eclipsed

For the second time in my life, I transformed ... but on that day, a decision sparked the dark powers of *The Equation*.

I waged a war upon the light and declared that I would conquer my subconscious by any means necessary. I would descend alone to its murky depths and suffocating heat with the *4 Rings* of *The Equation*, and win dominion over all its archetypes, treasures, innovations and second natures.

I would break all the mental barriers of the mind and reach my star ... not because of my color, not because of my class, not because of luck, not because of talent, not because of experience, not because of knowledge, not because of IQ ... but because of the abilities I would infuse into my character, like the blood that runs effortlessly through the veins.

The drive for triumph spread like a wildfire. I stood up ... and picked up a *plan*.

What the mind can conceive, the mind can achieve.

Hours upon hours accumulated into an experience of *accelerated expansion*. In less than 120 days, the lad had read over 50 books covering a broad range of diverse matters: Empires, *Leviathan*, *Paradise Lost*, Mr. Carnegie, the intricacies of currencies and securities, calendars, algorithms, and the mesmerizing codes of ancient civilizations.

The deepest subtexts would appear like faint lines running across the pages. *The Ring* of *Cosmic Energy* – The Ruby – instigated rushes of adrenaline. The nights would wear on with no need to sleep or eat. And if someone challenged, "Recite 12 lines on this random page" ... Well, the *darkness* has a way of surprising people.

As a curious scientist would drink a newly-invented cure before giving it to others, so the lad had to feel all the sides of *The Equation*.

Evolution usually happens gradually, yet research on foxes in Russia shows that *transformative* changes can make quantum leaps *quickly*.

Shock spread through the lad's body when he witnessed the Dark Science of *The Equation*.

Every morning he would scurry to the mirror to see how his body had changed. Brighter brown lines appeared in the irises of his eyes, cheek-bones raised up like 2 little hills, hands grew longer, and with the slightest training, muscles sharpened.

"What is happening here?" he wondered. "Can *The Equation* transform the way one *looks*?"

*A smart person judges a book by its content ... a genius figures it out by a **look** at the **cover**.*

The magical stallion flew the lad to meet a lord of wealth in Bulgaria. On a remote mountain in the city of Sofia, the lord shared with him the secrets of the Renaissance. And after the space between them was filled and shifted, the lord formulated a letter to open doors for the lad.

Along with 13 new letters of support ... he picked 13 scrolls full of new connections in different parts of world.

"I will work 100 hours with each passing of 7 days, over and over again," he vowed. And for the next 5 years, the lad never broke this *broken record.*

He erased everything from the past, and the clouds divided in the skies, signaling caveats and hazy omens. His roof became a prison. His spirit paid no heed to the pains around him.

And when these times left his eyes peering up at the crescent moon ... an ally came to check whether his soul's compass still pointed to the North Pole.

"What happened to my light? This is not who you are," Miriam said. "The Source of Light *destroyed* my dream and my *chance* to be happy," said the lad starkly.

"Son ... certain things in this world cannot be changed."

"Soon enough, my *decisions* ... will write their own future." He looked back up at the moon.

"The shoemaker does walk without shoes ..." the mother thought aloud.

"You discovered *The Equation*, yet you are blind to its meaning and you hurt your family."

"I have no family anymore. Soon I will never see you again."

A tear fell from the mother's eye. Miriam kissed her child on the forehead, whispering, "I will always love you, my light." And she handed the lad a letter and departed.

My dear son.

> *Will you hear my voice, my light?*
> *Will you hear my voice wherever the skies will carry you?*
> *Will you hear my prayers, my light?*
> *I, who will believe in you until the days run out of my life.*
> *I can still see the sad eyes of Omer, who now has changed into James.*
> *For rain falls on my city now, spreading out like black grass.*
> *Great distances shall separate us; times won't come back.*
> *Track the Milky Way, and may your lighthouse shine again.*

> *Good Night, my light.*

CHAPTER 25
The Dance of The Dragons

The magical stallion cruised through the clouds above the Atlantic Ocean. With the book *The Republic* on my lap, I reflected on how, before I boarded the plane, I saw a girl and a mother bidding each other farewell.

"I love you," the mother said. "And I wish you what is enough." The girl began to cry and replied, "I wish you too what is enough, Mother." After they had said goodbye, I approached the mother whose *tears* made her face look like a lake. "Excuse me, madam, may I ask what your blessing to your daughter meant?" The old lady smiled with wisdom and said heavily, "Look around … ambition and the desire to expand wastes the joys of life. All the heart needs is a bit of sun, some food, and the light of love."

"Why don't the flying animals have classes?" I wondered as the tight seat of my class was no match for the comfort of the seats in the elite class.

Tens of thousands of years ago, our human ancestors decided to migrate together to unknown parts of the planet, building the human empire through evolution.

They were flying dragons, whose looks, colors, and ways of speaking prompted no wars. As citizens of the world, they could easily adapt to changes in climate and concepts of time. They paved the way for humans today … to dance in the skies and fly to their Northern Star.

The plane landed on the Pacific coast of America.

Various vehicles meandering through the highway lanes made the landscape obscure.

Then, a horn sounded, and I saw Paul. Paul had been the guiding cornerstone during my odyssey on the Eastern Seaboard.

"Hi!" Paul shouted. As he was a famous player on the screen, 3 people approached Paul for his signature before I had even reached him.

"Hi Paul!" We hugged. "Thank you for picking me up."
"You look sharp, kid. How was your flight?" He inquired.

"Well … I flew with some dragons," I replied with a smile.
"Dragons! What is this … Camelot?" Paul laughed and we got in his car.
"Hey … I am proud of you, kid. I had no choice but to be born here. However, some do have a choice and decide to make the sacrifice to actually come here."

Paul's heart welcomed a near-stranger into his home. His house was my shelter for 3 weeks. Together we would travel and laugh … and a feeling of déjà vu would flash in my mind.

"I wish you luck, kid. My door is always open for you." I waved goodbye to Paul, and turned to the shadows of the night.

CHAPTER 26
The Planetary System of Cards

My new home was at the corner of an uninviting block. Barren and soot- colored streets served buildings with no lifts. Though my home was small – the bed room was also the study room – an influx of data shaped *my plan*.

The State of Play

One mystical midnight, I entered an elite lounge for the purpose of winning some bills and coins.

"I heard there is a chamber," I said to one suited concierge. "What is the password?" the man requested maintaining his unfixed gaze.

"Lady Luck," I replied.

The concierge escorted me to a private room where 15 other card players were present, engaged in chit chat.

One of the chamber's attendants approached me with a silver tray and elegantly inquired, "Might I offer you a drink or a cigarette, sir?"

"No thank you. Why drive a damaged carriage if I can drive my mind?" I tipped the old man and reflected on the ancient dynasties and civilizations which challenged the rules of cards.

The motion of rolling dice and people mulling about was halted when the host announced, "Ladies and gentlemen ... let the games begin!"

16 players sat around 4 mahogany tables. Checks, callings, and the order of spades, hearts, diamonds, clubs were *randomized* by shuffling the *decks* ... all of this movement tunneled into the dealer's declaration,

"Dear gentlemen, we have reached the final phase of the game, which means the winner shall take the pot."

The dealer began spreading the archetypal cards, linking them to *the moment.*

Turning up the cards, I started to connect their symbols to the Earth's calendar as well as to the number of days and weeks in a year.

An Asian man next to me calculated the odds and risks on a *logical* spreadsheet, while I had an ace up my sleeve.

Before the duke-like dealer dealt new cards, I focused my mental state. Cards represent the cosmic archetypes and shapes of the subconscious, astronomical objects orbiting in planetary systems.

When one unites their opposites into a symbiotic circle by *breaking* the barriers between them ... supernovas occur, releasing energy. One's mind can then channel these energies and reshape reality ... thundering the moment.

The tension began to tighten, as decisions dared to challenge *The Roulette of Fate.*

The dealer handed over new cards. The players were fiercely observing the eyes of their rivals to determine who told tales or truths.

In a clockwise direction around the table, the players took their turns. 2 players said, "All in" and revealed their cards. The Asian man next to me smiled with pride and said, "There's always a bigger fish." He revealed a Full House.

Silence swept the chamber, and I said, "Let's leave it to *luck*." I grabbed a Chance Cube and declared to everyone's surprise, "If it's *White*, you take all the winnings. If it's *Black* and my cards are better, you double the stakes."

Slowly, one by one, they nodded in approval. The Chance Cube was rolled ... and it showed black. I turned over my cards ... and smiled at the straight flush.

The lion is hungry – the need. An antelope appears – the desire.

There is a legend about a lord of wealth from Great Britain who, at the beginning of his aspirations, longed for some sort of a facility from which to work. Designing his future with *The Ring of Telescope Fear,* he decided upon a course of action and claimed a public telephone booth his own.

With this in mind, I went to an elite, elegant lodge. I paid the charges; but, instead of leisurely enjoying its fine facilities, I made it my own workstation.

In the meantime, my inner war with the Light was in motion; the pieces were moving along the chessboard to win the mental game.

From the sublime to the wildfire ... there is but a wire.

The plan was simple: to recruit people with great potential, a group that would trigger trades and translate the prosperities into presents for the poor.

As the circle of connections *expanded*, a note appeared in a newspaper. Streams of people, from varied cultures and accents, came to state their ideals and express the core of their character.

After contemplating their dates of birth and pondering their hidden potential ready be to unleashed, I picked up 6 young titans, some of the best men under the sun.

CHAPTER 27
The 7 Titans V

At the time they meant the world to me: 7 friends grouped together like glue. The first titan I nicknamed … *Mr. Smith*: a short, bulky man with full, wavy brown hair and big glasses. Quiet, observant to details, and with a great power of concentration, he could solve any problem with numbers.

A guilt-ridden merchant, he would negotiate even for an apple, and would always tune his ears when the radio sounded dangerous news.

The second titan was nicknamed … *The Sheik*. With an extravagant style and smooth, dark, Indian skin, he reigned over the word gambit. A magician at heart, he would perform exotic tricks with the Ace card he flipped between his fingers; the card his father gave him before he died.

The Phantom, the third titan, was a Celtic hunter, quick as the wind. Bald-headed and with bright green eyes, he was a pragmatist of few words. Honor and loyalty were his ax, though at times he appeared to be cold as steel.

The fourth titan was *Reds*. With hazel eyes, a pointy nose, perfect teeth, and street eloquence, he was extremely attuned to intuition. His conflicting characteristics included both wisdom and instinctive urges.

The tallest and most muscular of them all was *Atlas*. His dark eyes and long brown hair wrapped into a pony-tail, projected an aura of strength, like a man holding the globe.

B-rider was life's solo player. His motorcycle would speed his slim body to nature, and at the wrong moment he would tactlessly say, "By the way…"

Light travels faster than sound. That's why some people appear bright … until you hear them speak.
As diverse as the titans were, they always found unity in the variety of their colors.

One evening, as I was about to depart from the lodge, I felt that a part of the pie was missing – one wise titan was absent from the round table.

130

Suddenly a flare passed through the entrance. Wearing a striking silver suit, a golden tie and golden cufflinks inscribed with the word, *LIBERTY* ... we exchanged mystified looks. "Might I be of assistance?" I asked, feeling like I had seen the young man before.

"I am here for an opportunity," the young man said.

"Walk with me." I replied.

Women passing by us looked spellbound at his wavy golden hair, tanned face, Roman nose, sculptured jaws and deep blue eyes ... We sat down.

"How would you define a game changer mental state?" I asked. With the ease of a blink and effortless elegance, he said, "A leader approaches an intellectual and says, 'Let's do this and that.'
The intellectual follows, 'OK.'
'How much will it cost?' the leader wonders.
'100 golden coins,' the intellectual responds.
'100 golden coins!' The leader gasps. 'Can the gallows be worse?'
The next day the leader comes back to the intellectual with a greater vision and says, 'Let's do this and that.' The intellectual follows, 'OK.'
'How much will it cost?' the leader asks.
'200 golden coins.' the intellectual figures with fear.
The leader smiles and reshapes reality ... 'Let's get it done.'"

Clutching the safety belt of a roller coaster, I was stunned by his every syllable. And from that day on, the man who held a master certificate in charisma, was nicknamed ... *Jefferson*.

Some time before, I had met a person who seemed to be poor. I gave him a few coins. He smiled and replied, "I will never forget it, kid. Here is my card."

It turned out that his poverty was an optical illusion, for he was a wealthy man who desired to revisit the days when he was poor.

He owned many buildings in the metropolitan city and said, "Rest assured, your wish will be fulfilled."

We were all given a room, free of charge, that looked like a chancellor's workstation, furnished for assemblies.

The room was a magnificent space; it had a shiny black rectangular table at the center, 4 parallel stained glass windows, and a black piano.

One evening at dusk, we all assembled there for the first time. Lapel pins were spread on the table depicting the group's coat of arms: the symbol **V** formed by 5 circles of fire representing the 5 major continents of Planet Earth.

I stood up and said to the titans, "I can see the fear in your eyes, the same fear that lies in every living thing. One day the age of bravery might stand on the brink of destruction, and Hades might toast to our bones. But that is not this day. Today we stand up and conquer our minds!" One by one the titans stood up and exclaimed, "*For Victory!*"

CHAPTER 28
The Constitution

At the beginning, every voice was heard, and information ran like water between us.

Though we had established democracy … as *time* dragged on and *The Intellect System* started to balance numbers … the minds of the titans were just not *FREE*. Their hidden potential was occluded by confusion.

"How can I reach the settlements in the outskirts of their minds?" I pondered while walking through the shadows of the night.

Suddenly *The Ring of The Moment* shined its Emerald, and the Dark Science of *The Equation* picked up an idea.

I slipped some coins in the *machine*, picked up the payphone and called Jefferson.

"Hello?" he said sleepily, clearing his throat.

"Hi, it's me."

"What time is it?" Jefferson asked over the voices of women in the background.

"It does not matter … prepare the titans," I asserted.

"For what?" Jefferson yawned.

"We are all going to get a little wet."

During the darkest hours of the night, those hours which dread the dawn, we were all crunched like sardines in The Phantom's van, as it headed its way to the seashore.

Some titans complained about the chilling wind whipping their faces, but the purpose of the drive was soon attained. We had reached our destination: Poseidon's empire.

"You stay here," I said. "Jefferson … wait for my signal."

I descended through the rocks and sands. My face could feel the misty breeze from the waves. I gave the signal, and Jefferson sent Reds down to the shore.

"Hello, Reds," I welcomed.

"James, this frightens the hell out of me," he said with a shaking voice.

"Do you trust me?" I asked.

He nodded.

Going around him, I whispered, "I am going tie up your hands; stay calm." Slowly we entered the waters of the ocean. When more than half of our bodies were soaked wet, we stood still, and I said, "Look

at the stars, Reds." His chin lifted, and a *tragedy* attacked.
I pushed his head below the water's surface. Concentrating on his energy, my hands battled his *decision* to breathe again.

When I felt his heart had missed a beat, I let go, and a geyser of *tear drops* splashed out of the waters.

Reds had *awakened to life* and with cosmic energy, sped to the shore. There, he fell to the sand inhaling new air. I approached him and said,
"You see. The same sense of urgency you had to live … should be accelerated to win your future."

Jefferson, viewing from the hills above, directed B-rider to the shore.
"What is happening here?" B-rider asked.
"Oh nothing … we just felt like swimming."

When the mind is set free after a tragedy … the clock resumes ticking. If one then refuses to infuse *a new life* into the mind – to design destiny with a super-character – *The Intellect System* might strike again through a state of blindness.

I decided it was time to forge a scroll of wisdom derived from *The Equation*, so the titans would always have a guide at the turn of the tide.

"This endeavor should underscore the meaning of an *urgent* haste … for *time* is of the essence," I determined.

I called Jefferson and gave him a glimpse of the plan. Suddenly, he fell into one of the chairs in the chancellor's room and said, "I can't believe you are telling me that." He sat there, stunned. "Since I was 14, I have dreamt of writing a Constitution, something that is greater than me, beyond all limits. But when I told my friends, they framed it as arrogance. I say not! How can anything wonderful be done without this courage and ambition to dream? And what is there to be afraid of? *Failure* … hell, you can fall off a cliff for half the aspiration."

The warfare of the future is never won on the paper, but by picking up *treasures* from *the moment*.

For the next 7 days, Jefferson and I did not step out of the chancellor's room. Parchments, books, and pens seemed to shoot like time-lapsed clouds through dark skies.

134

Jefferson wrote on scrolls with the clarity and sharpness of a pane of glass. Battles and thunders of theories flashed so fiercely, that we began to fear that our minds would soon blast us into oblivion.

Jefferson would play the black piano, and the musical notes would summon the sounds of an orchestra.

At the end, we looked over our scroll, signed our names, and Jefferson wrote at the bottom ...

We offer these truths as universal evidence ... that if the human empire and the common wealth of our consciousness shall last for thousands of centuries ... living things will still say, "All dreams are destined for Greatness!"

"Did you always know?" I asked.
"No ..." Jefferson replied. *"But I believed."*

THE CONSTITUTION

✳ The Civil Code ✳

Article I
Honor and care for the elders. Do not cast them aside when their hair turns grey. Be their social insurance covenant, for they are not a remnant of the past, but rather orphaned children who have built the pillars on which we stand today.

Article II
Motherhood and childhood are the cornerstones of compassionate care. Not for nothing, they are the force that holds the world as does Mother Nature.

Article III
Respect those who migrate, for as proven by ancient history, they are bearers of our collective human evolution.

Article IV
Every child shall be granted free education. Furthermore, for the establishment of the rights to self-discovery, an innovative nature, and the pursuit of well-being, the child shall be entitled to liberating spiritual studies that engrave the good.

Article V
The inevitable tear that falls from the eye of a child is more powerful than any fleet or army on Earth, for it alone transforms the future and is the proof that evil does not exist.

Article VI
All human beings have the right to write the construction of their own character, unbounded by national origin. In Rome respect Romans, yet it will benefit all if the pin on your lapel is imported.

Article VII
Our consciousness, working in concert with the consciousness of the world, recognizes that luck and talent are inherent only in the equal honor of all and the bill of rights given to the followers of the human alliance.

Article VIII
Every aspiration emanated from the inner light of each member of the human family has equal opportunities for liberty, freedom of expression, dignity, and the infinite resources that power the progressive odyssey of realization. This provision shall be governed by the Universe's supreme court, the network of energy, and the moral compass instilled in each consciousness.

Article IX
Don't spit into the well from which you drink, for it is the prosperity of the planet.

Article X
We issue a moral order that one act of injustice anywhere is indivisible and thus shall steer the conscience of humankind to march in unity.

Article XI
The suspension of individual liberties in the name of Liberty creates an inevitable inequity. This imbalance arises from closed doors and arbitrary trade-offs, which stem from two propagandistic provisions concealed within contracts: the partisan and the presumptuous.

Article XII
No one nation, no matter how powerful, can cure all dangers. Hence, it is crucial to share sacrifice, information, and democratic duties, and to promote a partnership of progress. What defines us are neither our national borders nor our cultural identities, but rather our shared destiny.

Article XIII
Every human being promises to perpetually abide by the pledge birthed at the time of creation: to observe and protect, like a flying eagle, all fundamental freedoms encompassed by no other declaration than that which guides one's heart.

We offer these truths as universal evidence ... that if the human empire and the common wealth of our consciousness shall last for thousands of centuries ... living things will still say, "All dreams are destined for Greatness!"

THE CONSTITUTION

✳ The Corporate Code ✳

Article I
Human Evolution led to the human thumb. The
thumb led to precision. Precision leads to details. Details
lead to the 3 Fs: find the problem, fix it, finish it. The 3 Fs lead to
perfection, and perfection is only the beginning.

Article II
The Dreamer, The Doer, The Editor.

Article III
The ultimate reality is the infinite union of the mind: Tomorrow in the all-seeing
eye, Today in the moment, Yesterday in the subconscious.

Article IV
The stock exchange is the physical form of the network of energy. One move in
the chess game ... and everything changes.

Article V
Always let everyone know what you are thinking, for the famous bronze bull once
whispered that the best way to skyrocket profits ... is by unleashing a
fun surprise of dysfunction.

Article VI
Never address the vision as a label, for it shall not last. A timeless vision is a
mystical symbol. Fight not for a coin; fight for the heart.

Article VII
If you do not negotiate with the Universe at night, please do not negotiate for
profits in the morning.

Article VIII
Be joyful about the inevitable storms that tilt the ship. Be worried about the
people who steer it.

Article IX
A great czar sets sail beyond risk and the walls of the conglomerate, anchoring
instead in the mind. Those who decide to become enemies shall be
defeated not by data, but by innovation.

Article X
A plan is birthed by leaders yet perpetually evolved by the poorest soldier, who
sees the hidden longings stored in people's hearts.

Article XI
The easiest entities against whom to compete are giants. The bombardment of
data blocks news of the market. Once in a while it does not, and the chief states,
"Don't worry ... the reports show we are growing!"
The tallest skyscraper can be blocked by covering one's eye with a coin.

Article XII
The happiest moment of a game-changer innovation is when people suddenly
get anxious and say, "But it doesn't make any sense!"

Article XIII
The Golden Life Circle.
The empire begins. An air of legitimacy mingles with a parliamentary motion,
filling the vessel with energy. The loss of patience and the will's negotiation are
always met with opposing votes. The Universe storms ... a tear falls ...
the vessel breaks ... and the future is reshaped.

We offer these truths as universal evidence ... that if the human empire and the common
wealth of our consciousness shall last for thousands of centuries ... living things will still
say, "All dreams are destined for Greatness!"

CHAPTER 29
The Black Voltage

The titans were connecting the dots of the Constitution in our next assembly, when Jefferson called me over to a corner of the room. Looking at the Titans, he said, "Look at you guys … no sense of style." We saw eye to eye.

The next day, Jefferson wasn't present as 6 titans and I carried precious pictures with golden frames into the room. 7 black suits and sunglasses had been elegantly spread out on the black table.

"I have a good feeling about this," Atlas whispered. "Alright, gentlemen," Reds said. "Time to refine."

The Sheik turned some music on. And as we hung the last picture on the wall, Jefferson entered the room wearing his black suit and sunglasses. "Well, one thing is certain," he said with panache. "No one is perfect … and my name is no one." We smiled and cackled with glee … we were ready to thrive – "*For Victory!*" the titans cheered.

Mr. Smith and I established the course of action and shaped a plan that would transfer prosperities to the poor. We visualized the schema as 4 concentric circles, engraved by a scribe-compass on a black stone. The letter *G* was carved in the center.

The first circle of action was the collection of bottles. Recruits would bundle bottles from dawn to sunset. The second circle of action drew chefs who would place bags of food on the corners of alleys, which the Phantom would then pick up.

"The slightest variations in global currencies can change the margins of prosperities." Mr. Smith pointed to the next circle. He would play with the prosperities in various markets, exchanging them … at the right moment in *time*.

The fourth circle was the train of information. Skimming through piles of books and notes, we would transform the information into scrolls.

Then, we would offer to transfer these scrolls to different enterprises.
"How shall these scrolls grow my prosperities?" presidents would ask with appraising, critical eyes. Jefferson's charisma would smile

and jest … "The proper time to influence the character of an enterprise is about 100 years before it is born."

*V*ictory after victory came our way, and everything seemed to move around us like a whirring carousel.

Traders and mercenaries would meet our black suits, and the golden rays of the sun would flash against our black sunglasses, and the *V* lapel pins would propel exclusive handshakes and gazes upon the titans.

One cold night, the moon emerged from behind the clouds, and we all drove to one of the lightless parts of the city.

We were spread out in various vehicles, and radio transceivers with little antennas opened a portable line for speech.

Poor people with long, shaggy manes of hair were whispering with sore throats. Hooded figures were crawling across the gloomy grounds.

"Look at that, guys," B-rider said. "Yeah … this is the doorstep of *darkness*," Atlas replied in an icy voice.

Slowly the titans emerged from the vehicles. Carrying bags, they handed them over to the desperate people panting for breath.

Enclosed within the car, I stared … at the glare of *the moon*.

Later that night, fried fish, potato chips, toast, and boiled brown eggs were laid on the table of a restaurant. The chef said, "As always, this is on me, guys."

Jefferson wooed 3 ladies near the dance floor, his charms pitter-pattering into their hearts, while Reds breached the silence that engulfed the table. "Would you say that Man is a born thief? He steals the trees from nature, the eggs from the chicken, the honey from the bees, so why not steal the success of the Intellect and give it back to the Spirit?"

The Phantom sighed … "Just the right amount of wrong."

CHAPTER 30
A Ballad of Brothers

I drove the titans hard ... but one should drive oneself the hardest. *The Rings* of *The Equation* grew stronger and darker, allowing me to be awake for several days straight. Working from dawn to dawn, I ate only tiny meals, for a body can live on inner energy.

If my war with the light was suspended at times, it was with brother Jefferson at the villa of one of the wealthiest lords in history.

"*Liberty! Fraternity!*" Jefferson would yell lifting our flag emblazoned with a golden *V*.

After 21 years of having no friends on this planet ... suddenly, in the depths of the darkness, I had found a candid brother and 6 titans.

The villa's view was breathtaking. Its sweeping lawns and statues kindled the light of adventure in our eyes.

Jefferson was a great artist. With a pencil he would paint epic worlds of expeditions and battles.

Two youths full of dreams ... we imagined the oceans of the world full of ships blessed by Britannia, bearing armies of astronomers, archeologists, and scientists. On the ship's deck, Jefferson triumphantly held The Constitution, as the sun beckoned us to lost kingdoms.

In the spirit of a chivalrous knight from long ago, Jefferson would break a piece of bread and spread the crumbs on his sleeve.

Seconds later, the birds would fly to him, and he would tie missives to their legs.
"What wish did you write there?" I would ask curiously.
The birds would spread their wings and soar up and away in a network of energy ... and Jefferson would reply ...

Let Destiny Go With Those Who Dare.

CHAPTER 31
State Space X

My friend Jefferson adhered to a piece of wisdom engraved on the tomb of a great thinker: "I am not an advocate of frequent changes in laws and constitutions, but with the change of circumstances … institutions must advance to keep up with *the pace of time.*"

It is easy to change units of intellectual data in the consciousness, but worlds harder to *decide* to *transform* the mind.

At the time, the lad bit the bait and believed that intellectual data and spiritual omens were both confusing forces. The lad was blind to the fact that intellectual messiness is the accumulation of bad decisions, while omens sent by the Universe are guiding stars for those whose eyes are *free.*

One night he drove to a desert alone. There he contemplated not the stars, but the expansion of space, the accelerating universe: *Dark Energy* and *Dark Matter.*

The war with the Light was triggered, and the lad said; "Your forests speak in messy omens. No wonder nothing is clear. And now … drums, drums in the deep. The ground shakes. And the moment is the deep breath before a plunge."

The lad sped back to the chancellor's room. He flung the door open. The titans sprang to their feet, and the lad whispered … "We need to *EXPAND.*"

One night, the titans and I were sitting around the black table as the rain fell from the kingdom of the sky. Mr. Smith was knitting numbers; The Sheik was pondering, playing with his Ace card; Atlas was drinking coffee; and Phantom, B-rider and Reds were trying to fix a broken light.

Thunder bolted through the heavens, and Jefferson opened the door. His face was ghostly pale, like he hoped to die another day. "Hey. Where were you, Jeff?" B-rider asked.

"Yeah, you and I often drink coffee together in the evening," Atlas added.

A sense of something that could not be undone spread through the room.

"Quite frankly, I care far less where you were," Mr. Smith reckoned.

141

"As long as it doesn't threaten the iron power of my profits."

"Well … that depends on how you discern good from bad," Jefferson countered.

"Jefferson, you're troubled. What happened?" I inquired.

"Does a well-intentioned deed lose its value if it's not exalted?" Jefferson asked.

"What!" B-rider exclaimed.

"If the answer is yes, how do we know what the future will unfold?" Jefferson made way for the moment.

"Jefferson, you walk on enemy lines. Just tell us what happened." Mr. Smith's nostrils flared.

"A contact was made, and one lord of wealth is willing to meet us."

"I don't see any bad in that," Atlas said.

"Well … the man has a way of pulling strings," Jefferson added.

"This is not going to be perfectly splendid," Reds said *darkly*.

"What does this man do?" Mr. Smith inquired.

"He is an exporter, as far as I know," Jefferson said.

"There is more to this than meets the eye, I sense." The Phantom was hunting his own intuitions.

"I hold to your oath Jeff; you promised we will not enter the twilight." B-rider challenged … and hostile voices followed.

"Wait! Back to square one," I paused. "Many beacons we admire today *decided*, at times, to take advantage of the *darkness* to reach where they *desired*. So, gentlemen, study the battleground carefully: you are going to have a part to play on it."

And The Sheik flipped his Ace card … "I fear some *other* forces will have a part to play there too."

It was night, and upon dining on my favorite dinner dish – bread and water – I considered that the action was to take place at the lord's court.

From this mental *disadvantage* … I picked up an *advantageous* plan. The lord was of Austrian descent, and from the stories of history, a plan sparked to mind. One studies the past so as to reshape the future and then takes risks that stream against the currents of the river.

Meanwhile, the titans were impatiently waiting in the street. Sterner than ever, they sent Reds to speed things along.

"James, it is getting late; we should be there shortly," he said, attempting to quicken the pace.

Sitting in the darkness of the room, I replied, "My watch is wound to be 40 minutes behind. So that the illusion of time will stand upon the edge of a knife, not the mind."

The lampposts were glowing against the cars' windows. Everything moved in *slow motion*, and I said, "Jefferson ... this is going to be a fine night."

The titans shut down the engines and exited the vehicles. "We are here," Atlas said. There was the feeling that we were being watched. Nothing could be heard besides the rustling of the leaves and drops of water descending from the heavens. Our *V* lapel pins were blazing as we halted at the entrance hall. "Is this a mansion or a castle?" Jefferson wondered upon looking at the scope of the structure.

The guards' eyes scanned us, and we entered the realm of things that have not yet come to pass.

The domain of the mansion was magnificent. My gaze was wandering across the peculiar purple velvet curtains and decorations that sparkled with silver and pearly spikes... when the lord sounded his voice, "Haa ... at last."

After he exchanged greetings with the titans, the lord's manners met the hand of Jefferson, thinking he was me. Jefferson smiled a little, and the lord's eyes caught sight of me. "I don't think we were introduced." I replied, "Good evening, sir. My name is James."
The confusion thickened like fog, when the lord asked, "What can I offer you? I have Brandy, Rum ..."
"I thank you, but we don't drink," I said.
Looking to his guard, the lord mumbled, "They don't drink, eh?"

He poured himself a brown ale and said, "Sit, sit ... is there anything else I can offer you?"
Some titans called for coffee, the lord signaled, and the plan moved forward.
"So ... I accepted your request to see me." The lord said enigmatically.
"Might I correct that you were the one to summon us this night." I said. The lord's snowy beard, fierce face and heavy weight ... all seemed to smile.

"Do you know who I am?" The lord said to the titans frozen with fear. I nodded, and he continued, "I need brains like you guys. There are many markets out there, but few people thinking."
"What is our return?" Mr. Smith's interests challenged.
"Never ask for the reward before you know your task," the lord

counseled. as the golden coffee service tray was laid on the table. "So …" The lord's eyes were piercing. "Will you be the sheep or the wolf?"

The 6 titans were conducting a cordial conversation with the surrounding guards, Mr. Smith was bargaining with the lord, and I was alone, pacing back and forth.

The chess pieces were placed in the right spots.
A good while later, Mr. Smith and the lord were beginning to get tangled up in the numbers of *The Intellect System*. And when the point of make or break arrived, *the moment of decision* … rage ignited.

I tossed the golden coffee tray thorough the near-by sliding glass door and shouted, "This is what will happen to you! Your enterprises are nothing but a broken backbone, accustomed to weakness."

The guards thrust the titans back, ready to strike, but the wealthy lord signaled them stop. "All of you … leave us," he commanded.

Slowly the parlor emptied. The lord stood up and addressed me, "Go to the garden, wait there."

Passing through the shattered glass door, I entered the large garden and beheld its glimmering fountains.

"I should have you whipped for your impudence," the lord said as he approached from behind. His cane displayed a precious gem on its edge.
"We are not enemies but friends," I said. "Though passions may have strained, I don't think they should break the bond of our affection."

The lord replayed the past … "I've heard that line before."
"We all have." I said. "Sir, not long ago, I am sure you can *remember*, you strived for someone to assist you. I want you to assist me now."
"What do you want?" the lord said, threatening *the will*.
"50," I replied.
"50 what?" the lord said coldly.
"50 and 4 more zeroes," I stated.
"And what will I get in return?" the lord *negotiated* impatiently.
"Nothing but your youth back."
"And how will I do that, I wonder?" The lord maintained his

144

fixed gaze.

"Tonight you will sleep in peace," I stated calmly. "You will remember the days when you were poor and your tears cried for success."

Chiefly for the sake of hiding his secret, the lord turned his back to me and wiped *a lonely tear* with a handkerchief. "Wait here," he whispered.

Several minutes later, the lord returned to the garden carrying a silver suitcase. "I see what you say. Here ... take this case. You won't find all of what you wanted but it is more than enough. Go ... leave me now." I bowed my head and departed the garden.

CHAPTER 32
The Floodgates of Fire

A figure from history, who had rewritten the future by assembling parts to shape moving vehicles, once doubled the prosperities for his artisans. This act *designed* a new market and a new luck for *destiny*.

The past rippled its effect and inspired me to split the prosperities evenly between myself and the titans. Nevertheless, some things that should not have been forgotten ... *were lost.*

The titans were in the chancellor's room thriving on the winnings for which they sacrificed. Suddenly, the smell of smoke swirled up through the window, rapidly alarming them, their temperatures dropping.

When they couldn't find the lad, they climbed down the stairs, and in the back lot they saw him standing before a bonfire.

Voices fell silent ... and there ... the fire was burning the lad's bills.

The Dark Science of *The Equation* ignited all *The 4 Rings*, and the mind began to vibrate. A mighty mental dam broke ... and the forces of the subconscious were unleashed.

The subconscious had become a cannon, bombarding the banks of the consciousness with bullets it could not deflect, like a cup overfilled with water, or a shore flooded by a roaring tsunami.

I would walk down the street and my mind would calculate the distance between all the lampposts. Books were memorized by heart, and thoughts raced in an infinite loop.

Uncontrollably, upon every tick of the clock, my mind picked up treasures and innovations from the subconscious: scientific sketches on machines predicting earth quakes; clocks generating energy to produce perpetual motion: maps of secret tunnels within the great pyramids.

My decision to conquer the subconscious threatened to become my undoing. For now there were no lights on, and my inner light, the compass, was too many light years away to guide the way through the wildfire.

Shields were shattered, spears were splintered … and this inner *tragedy* reminded me that I might lose the fine sight of orchards blossoming, birds nesting, robins and squirrels among the trees, the taste of berries, and the naked grass.

Trees would fade and nightfalls in the winter would come without the morning star … life would be a barren wasteland riddled with ash and dust.

And when I thought that things could not get any worse, a gloating shark appeared with a greedy grin.

"Hello?" I answered the phone, clearing my throat.

"James …" the shark jeered while smelling the *blood*. "What is *up*?!"

"Nothing," I replied. "I am just tired a bit."

"Well, you sound bad. Do you need anything?" the shark formulated a *Faustian offer*.

"No, I will manage," I said.

"All right, mate. I just don't want anything bad happening to my golden egg, eh? At any rate, my friends and I want to expand your circle of actions. We think that through us, you guys will do much better; the difference in size will be day and night. Are you interested?" the shark said darkly. Coughing, I muttered a cloak of uncertainty.

"Er …"

"I am quite surprised. Nevertheless, you have 7 days before the pegs in my château won't hang your coats."

The *tragedy* took a strange twist when it seemed that the door that navigates one's *decisions* ... was wrenched off its hinges.

The right – the free will – to make decisions was fractured. I would connect 2 die together with a string, roll them, and then calculate the the numbers to see if a decision matched the network of energy.

On the 7th night, the titan's eagerness to fight met a steep slope, when I said to Jefferson with a weak voice, "You go without me." "What reason will we give for your vacant seat?" Jefferson asked. "I don't know … I feel like the poles are shifting their axis."

CHAPTER 33
Transformation Triumph

Alone, on the way back home, I felt as though a black hole had taken hold over life, and now *tears* ran from my eyes like falling stars, filling my heart with a new hope.

Time started to move in slow motion.

Sitting on the edge of a chair, I stared at the stark walls, engulfed by the darkness of the night, and at my watch, which decided not to spin.

Suddenly, I missed the hearty laugh of my family, my aunt who had passed away, my old roof, and the soft feeling of a kiss on the cheek.

I laid my head down, a *tear* descended, and I fell asleep.

That night, the windmills of time delivered a dream.

> *The streets were empty as my old car speeded.*
> *Blurry bluish wind was blowing, whirling the windmills of time.*
> *When the light turned green, instead of heading straight, I turned left.*
> *A tree passed by, the wind charged harder, and*
> *the car struggled to climb The Avenue of the Stars.*
> *I exited the car on The Galaxy. The wind turned white*
> *when eyes looked up and saw an orb of light circling itself.*
> *In the twinkling of an eye my legs were in the center of the orb.*
> *Infinite bricks of light were beaming in the orb, bathing my being.*
> *A brick burst into shards; a little crystal emerged, hovering forward.*
> *My hand was extended to reach it, and a touch absorbed lost information.*

I opened my eyes.

The fresh breath of rebirth ... and suddenly I whispered, "Jefferson ... no."

At once, I rushed forward and let my fingers dial Jefferson's number.

Moments passed, and it seemed that no person was present ... then, "Hello?" Jefferson whispered.

"Jefferson, did you sign the papers?" I asked urgently.

Thinking, he replied, "No ... but Mr. Smith is about to sign any second now."

"No! Stop him," I said.

"What? Why?" Jefferson was caught by surprise.

148

"Do not trade anything. Abort the mission," I told him.

"James ... but ..."

"Jefferson, please ... call it off. Go... and wait for my letter"

If only I could have been there when Jefferson read the letter to the titans, just to hug them, and say how their friendship had filled my life.

Dear Titans

> *Honorable men you are with stout hearts.*
> *I am about to embark on a spiritual road.*
> *I wish I knew when I might return.*
> *For 7 months now you have been laboring day and night.*
> *Truly nothing can dampen your spirits.*
> *Live the great joys of life, and soon we shall meet again.*
> *Yours Deeply*

The Republic of Revolution

The war with The Source of Light was over, and perpetual peace sprouted to life.

After years of aspiration and searching, the dream had lit my inner lighthouse, showing me the shores of my future.

Though the war was over ... the devastation remained, waiting for the individual to amend.

The republic of revolution is a ribbon of liberty ... the waging of a revolution within oneself for the purpose of signing a treaty of peace among all the powers of the mind: *a union for evolution.*

This revolution guides every human being, at one point or another, to conduct a series of *negotiations* and conversations from within, so as to challenge destiny and the ideals of one's dreams.

It was time for me to do the same, for though I had transformed for the third time in my life, transformation is only the beginning. Together with the subsequent series of decisions, it reshapes reality into higher *triumph.*

Wearing *The 4 Rings* of *The Equation* as mental armors, I pondered, "Against whom shall I wage my inner revolution?"

Then it occurred to me ... like the appearance of a centaur crossing a black lake. I decided to challenge the dark lord of *The Intellect System* ... the Ego.

Wearing a toga and a flimsy shawl thrown over my torso, I aligned my spine, struck a meditative pose … and entered the empire of the mind.

As an arctic explorer under heavy cold clouds, my consciousness opened a great gate, a mental portal, and sensed an ice-like land.

Aurora borealis glowed in the skies, bright red as ripe strawberries. My consciousness reached a cold cavern with hieroglyphic markings engraved on iridium.

I concentrated my consciousness and entered the cave.

It seemed as though a sleeping giant had awoken, as temples of gold and ancient treasures were protected by leopards ready to leap.

Then, I saw the dark lord. Surprisingly, the dark lord had a pale face and wore simple clothes, but on the arms of the chair stood golden goblets.

"I want to know the truth!" I demanded.

"So why do you come here? The truth is everywhere," the Ego replied with a hoarse, throaty voice.

"Everywhere! How would you know?" The interrogation continued.

"Simple," the Ego said. "Everything on earth reveals the past, the present and the future, and we are here because of this energy trade."

"We?!" I exclaimed. "You blind people with pride. Because of your stratagems, people lose precious joys."

"Remember that you are entitled to your opinion, but not your own facts," the Ego cautioned.

"It still doesn't change anything," I said. "You deceive people."

Suddenly the Ego replied with an ire more fierce than fire, "Do not count me as a conspirator of cheap tricks! All your life you were pointing fingers, calling me a false ally. I am not a puppeteer. *I don't do that!*"

"But aren't you the reason people live in cages for ages?" I wondered.

"Well … legends are often misread," the Ego calmly said, "Egoism begins when one makes a bad decision. Only then do I hack into the mind and blind it with foolish fairytales like luck, talent, IQ. I imprison the mind and define a reality that is based on limits. I claim lordship over the will as you forfeit your life to vanity. I sign a treaty with the subconscious, and while you think you laugh all the way to the bank, we just sit and laugh."

"So how are you a part of the fellowship of the mind?" I asked. "I am a force of Go!" the Ego said. "First unbind the blindness of your eyes, *transform*, and you shall see that I am a force of determination, a daring horse that can take you wherever you want. But when you apply my powers for selfish gains, I become wild, and you will break your spine.

Compete within you for the toughest challenges, like uniting the spiritual and the physical, and when you make your decisions altruistic, then will all the powers of *accelerated expansion* come to your aid. Nothing will stop you; you will be like a comet in space that transforms higher and higher, challenging gravity."

"*The Equation* says that a tragedy is the trigger for transformation. Why suffering?" I asked.

"It is never about the suffering, nor the fairytale of evil," the Ego assured.

"No birth is possible without the forces of resistance. Like the seed that cannot sprout without fire. A tragedy is a present in disguise."

"Why then is there a clash between the spiritual and the physical world?" I asked.

"Well ..." The Ego said. "Why is there a clash between billionaires and spiritual masters? They are opposite sides of the same coin. One brilliantly moves the wheels of the physical world, and the other brilliantly moves the wheels of the spiritual world."

"How can the present be purified?" I asked.

"Among the world's sages, there are none like the person next to you," the Ego said. "Success is indivisible; the success of anyone anywhere is the success of everyone everywhere. It is entirely up to you to see that every force is a force of light, and you are given one right and one responsibility."

"What are they?" I said.

"No destiny is certain, but the inherent right that one has to design the future is. And the supreme responsibility is to always evolve your destiny for the greater good of all living things."

"How do you know all of that?" I wondered.

"Don't forget," the Ego smiled. "As of now, I own many lives. I can see what their hearts already know, but their eyes are blind to. Let me tell you a story of long ago. One startling secret dawned with the cradle of civilization: great mental powers and powers of technology, which were lost over time. Now the mind limits itself to folklores; mirrors to an ancient colony full of treasures waiting to be rediscovered and transform the times forever."

Suddenly the ice caps and glaciers started to shake as the Ego thundered,

"So it is time to transform! And cry ...

FREEDOM!"

The rest of the 40-day meditation was nirvana ... an oasis of shafts of delicious lights that shone like stars illuminating in the night.

At the end of the spiritual journey, after transcribing the dream, I turned the knob, and for the first time in my life ... I was truly fulfilled.

The birds were chirping from the branches of the trees, the skies were burning bright blue, the sun was dancing on the water, and the warm breeze of spring was appeasing to the lungs.

Suddenly, I seized *the moment*. My old vehicle drove to the city of planes. There, the magical stallion flew me to the other side of the continent.

I landed, and a vehicle took me to a mystical museum, the place that lights the hero, Crossing the Delaware.

Like fireworks, I burst into joy, and ran to the steps leading up to the museum.

I climbed them, holding Atlantis inked on a parchment, a symbol, a speech, and one other little thing.

I lifted my hands, jumped into the air, and shouted to the surrounding strangers, "I did it! I did it! ... *FULFILLMENT!"*

152

PART 4

THE RETURN OF THE LIGHT

CHAPTER 34
The Infiniteth Lifetime

This story began 55 years ago, and now a lad was close to his 22th birthday.

The Ring of The Moment endowed by *The Equation*, reveals parallel universes where every present moment is in great gratitude to the past.

Just as the sword is forged by the fire of the blacksmith, and as decorative stained glass is heated by hellish temperatures ... the lad was molded anew, thankful to the Dark Science of *The Equation*. Never again would he ask, "Who am I?" or "What is my future?"

There are no evil forces; evil is created only when one decides to create it. All multicolored powers in the Universe work in perfect synchronicity for mutual prosperity.
During the dark days, one bleeds while climbing the thorns of the rose. Then when enlightenment is reached, the mind can take on *expanded* perspectives of life.

From the ashes of fire, life shall arise anew.
From the shadows of the night, guiding light shall ignite.
A sword that was shattered shall fight again for a transformed future.

The lad grasped a big box, and traveled to the shore of the sea.

The night was dark, and the box had gathered the dust of bad decisions. The lad ambled towards the ebbing waters. He let the box be a bygone boat and said, "This is for you, Charon. Tell your fictional boss The Light says hello."

"Hello?" The phone line transferred Jefferson's voice.
"Hey, it's me." I replied.
"James ... where were you? We were worried," Jefferson said.
"I am here now, dear brother."
"When can I see you?" Jefferson implored. "I feel like it has been ages."
"Jefferson, please summon the titans ... this will be the final address."

The door of the chancellor's room was open, and there my friends rushed to hug me, asking why my going away had changed the age of my face.

"I missed you too, guys," I replied, looking at them as the rocks and blocks of loyalty. "Please have a seat. I want to share something."

We all sat around the black table. A stillness was filling the hills of my Heart. I stood up and said, "I really don't quite know what to say. I can just remember that, as a boy ... I would take my binoculars and see if the street would send me a friend. The 7 of you are the harvest after years of wishing. But this day marks the end of our actions." Like a flickering flame, Reds asked, "But what about our work, the ideals?"

"We have achieved much together," I said. "If you quiet your ears, you will hear ghostly hopes wandering at night, whispering 'I could have stood up for the light.' We are so diverse, yet shared hopes united us. We fought for the ideal that every dream deserves a shot. So let your hearts be at peace, because it's better to have lived one brave day than a lifetime of ifs."

"What will we do now?" The Sheik asked.
"Well ... I know we will always stand by one another," I said. "When it is swelteringly hot, or when the teeth chatter in the cold."
"Where will you go?" B-rider wondered.
"A time comes when every man sees a new dawn." I believed. "A new beginning awaits me. Although it's bright, failures and loneliness will be like distasteful medicine that the body needs in order to climb."

Suddenly, Atlas stood up, approached me, and said, "I am here for you." The titans followed, all but Jefferson, his eyes sad yet hopeful.

As I was about to wave goodbye, the titans said together, "Hey, James." I turned, and my friends declared, "*For Victory.*"

I bowed my head and, as the sands of time carried me to the verge of bidding farewell, Jefferson seized the moment to say, "You are the best friend I have ever had."
I hugged him as if life might take him away forever.

"I know a day will come ... and we will meet again," Jefferson said. "By the fresh breath of liberty ... you are the greatest man I know," I said. Our eyes started to tear, and we together recited,

"We offer these truths as universal evidence ... that if the human empire and the common wealth of our consciousness shall last for thousands of centuries ... living things will still say, 'All dreams are destined for Greatness!'

The Chariot

Not every dynamic that occurs in the Universe is in accord with a set of systematic laws. Sometimes the mere observation of a universal law can, by itself, cause change.

The future is a constant of *infinite transformations*. Like the clouds on a midsummer day ... things come into being, and things pass from being. That means that if one waits for the future to come ... one will miss *something*.

Now the lad could see the shores of his future lit by The Source of Light, but he had no idea what the first step might be.

Dear Mother
Words describe not the pangs of my heart missing you.
Your voice alone can spur my spirit to see the stars.
What shall I say? What shall I write? Bad decisions were
strands of fog drifting across the skies of my life.
But now, for the first time, I see what the future might be.
There was a spark! I felt the earth was fleeing from
beneath me, as my inner desires were carried higher and
higher into the skies by 4 horses flying a white chariot.
I am coming to see you Mother. I hope I shall discover the
*first step of the Eq**way**tion.*
With Unconditional Love

James

After replenishing a small stock of provisions, the lad entered the city of planes.

With a suitcase on a tricky cart, he walked down the boarding corridor. And the magical stallion soon roared to life.

156

At supper in the summer, my family and I were dining around the table.

As laughs and smiles were floating, and the frying pan was nicely hissing, my mother looked at the ring she had given me a long time ago, *The Star of Light*, and whispered, "Do you *remember?*"

"Yes," I replied. "Between the Column and the Star."

On the mantelpiece were pictures from the past. Memories beckoned a *tear* from my eye as I pondered how time had passed by and precious moments had been lost.

There I also saw my old melodic nightlight. I opened it, and the ship was still sailing in the skies towards a lighthouse. The nostalgic melody swirled around me like snow-flakes. And then I decided to lay it to rest … the fear of the dark was overcome.

Beneath the blanket, I woke up at the moment the sun dawned over the horizon. My old house was glimmering in the sun's beams, warm as a candlelight. I then placed my gaze on the green field in front of the house. A barometer of *beauty*, the grass seemed greener, *younger yet older*. Bushes blossomed, and flowers and ferns filled the field.

Then, motherly foot-steps came towards me.

"I missed you, Mother."

"I missed you too, my light," Miriam replied warmly.

"I don't know what to do now, Mother. Isn't it funny? That one can see the path, yet be blind to the first step."

"The challenge is like a living organism … always growing," she explained.

"What about the enterprise you told me about?"

"Yeah …" I said, shrugging my shoulders. "Its concept is just big, and I have no training. Perhaps it would be prudent to put it on the shelf for now."

My mother smiled and pulled me into a hug. "Calm your heart, young one."

"Before the end of any expedition, answers drip from the unseen … and all one needs to do is to pick them up."

Those days of frailty often found me playing games with my young cousins in my grandmother's large garden.

With their blue eyes and straight bright hair, these elves would invest hours together running along the sweeping lawn and hiding behind the trunks of tropical trees. "A minute with the wisdom of a child,"

I thought, "is parallel to a year spent in the biggest library."

"Please don't leave us," one of my cousins beseeched me. "Yeah, now there will be no adults who want to play with us," added another child.

"Can we tell you a little secret about grown-ups?" my cousin asked.

"Yes," I said.

"But do you promise not to say?" she whispered. "They will punish us."

"Yeah, I promise," I replied.

"Alright," She giggled, and the other children came closer. "We call them the Boomerang Bomb."

"Yeah," another child chuckled, covering his mouth with his hand. "They throw the boomerang ... and forget it comes back."

Reversing to the Future.
Then, as these bewitching elves were giggling, the wind in the garden suddenly began to whirl, and the limbs of the trees swayed gently in the breeze.

This vision triggered a memory, a piece of wisdom about the circle of life. "How many with whom I came to this world have already left it?"

In the years to come ... on a sacred day, my grandfather Mati said, "I am proud of you, Son." With the next dawn, while I was far, far away ... he crossed to the afterlife. Then, *The Ring of The Fountain of Youth* reminded me that, decades before, his *tragedies* led people to reason that he could never have children.

Yet Mati *transformed* the lemon into lemonade by writing a new, brighter future.

Back to the present, I decided, "I will follow the circle of life. I will travel to the holy city, as my grandfather did, and pray to discover the first step of my new path."

The glow of the sunset sank in the west, casting highlights of golden amber.

The imagery of the holy city sent a rush of sensation down my spine, as Miriam and I walked on its streets.

The place was oozing with mystery; ancient sites revealed priests preparing for rituals, ivory horns were blowing, foundation stones were engraved with Aramaic, the exotic vegetables in the markets were richly varied, and cloaked strangers were sounding the secret of the hidden world.

We arrived at the tomb of a great king.
It seemed as though the place inseparably interconnected *the opposites*. *Spirituality* and *Geometry* were united in a pair of equilateral triangles, forming joint reflections.

I reached my hand forth to a tomb and wished, "I am here on behalf of the life I love. Many years ago, my grandfather was here wishing for a son. Well ... now I need a little help here, for I am blind to my first step."

If there is any entrepreneur out there ... who thinks that only academia and the intellect can launch an epic enterprise ... the heart of a lad cries that the mind will be free to see otherwise.

That very night, the lad *decided* to sleep on his old roof under the stars of the universe; and a dream brought to life the enterprise about which his mother had inquired.

Though blurry, and with no clear model, the dream revealed exotic superheroes, other worlds, costumes, cards, and 2 manuscripts.

Pure hope swept, as though a *failing* fighter vowing not to falter, and for the rest of the night, the lad interpreted the insights and transcribed them onto a parchment.

The host of the skies, the moon hung over the horizon. Sitting on my roof, I was contemplating the road ahead, when my mother came to offer cookies.

"What are my choices, Mother?" I asked. "Well ..." she said. "It is for you to determine the direction of the day. You can stay here ... at home with the family, and worries of security will never haunt you. You will have sons and daughters who will love you. But if you travel towards your North Star, years of sorrow will trail you like your shadow. For life ... is sometimes the first casualty of destiny. And I will miss kissing you good night."

CHAPTER 35
The Path Passed

The magical stallion landed on the Pacific coast of America. If one hides from the path that leads to one's fulfilling future, it is as if one is fearful of death.

Death is a part of life, enhancing the free exchange of energy among all living things. When a star explodes after playing its role in the universe, its cosmic rays and remains enrich the formation of new star systems.

At the time, though I knew my first step, its magnitude required all the reservoirs of breath from my being. Suddenly I was all alone in this world ... and fear detoured my path, steering me to bad decisions.

But because every force in the Universe is a force of light, the path we take to escape destiny ... is often the way to *evolve* it.

The Equation reveals that every human being has layers of destinies, vessels ready to be filled with energy. When a vessel is full, a supernova takes place, and the destiny, the will ... is achieved.

I went backwards to one of my former layers of destiny: a performer. Though friends from other fields tried to refine *the path*, door after door was shut ... day after day.

Next to me, young dreamers from across the globe, who had crossed the oceans of the Earth for an opportunity, hoped to fulfill their lives by actualizing their aspirations ... yet their rainbows would drain of color.

Fatigue engulfed the dreamers as they sent packages, made their private stories public, and were dusted aside when they differed from stock characters.

Once upon a time, the daughter of a wealthy man got sick. When the news spread across the village, everyone came to offer comfort.

People prayed for the health of the girl from sunrise to sunset. The girl was cured, but to their surprise ... the father was crying. Finally, they managed to ask why, and the wealthy man replied, "I wonder now ... if the sons of the poor could have been saved?"

After a *tragedy transforms* … one becomes more sensitive to energy. The mind no longer falls short. The need to steal mental energy from a stranger next door ceases to exist … For one can win with the infinite sources that lie within.

While skies thick with clouds, I would wander through the streets and the city's disheveled shelters.

Poor people pray that strangers won't turn a blind eye to them and will help blaze their path. I would often sit down with them and ask, "What are your *dreams*? How do you see the world? What is the meaning of *love* to you?"

Their eyes would grow wide, with a floating sense of utopia as they felt that, deep down, everyone cares for them.

"For me, love is to receive and send energy," one blind lady said.

"When 2 strangers meet, at the same time and the same place. And together they don't just appreciate the beauty in one another, but they seize *the moment* and explore what messages the Universe tries to tell them."

It was during that time that I met an angel. Her name was Jasmine.

She was an alumna of one of the 6 Ivy League Schools that denied my childhood dream, and so a miracle emerged from *tragedy*.

She had long brown hair, shining hazel eyes, and a compassionate spirit … and in the blink of an eye, we loved one another as human beings.

3 days after my 22nd birthday, as we approached the altar to take our vows, I asked her, "Why did you agree to marry me?"

And she replied, "It is not our experience that defines us, but the ideals we decide to embrace."

CHAPTER 36
The Coliseum of Miracles

I was back in the ring of life to fight for my future.

What I had thought to be *a bad* decision that detoured me from my path … was actually the way to strengthen it, for every force in the Universe is a force of *good*.

However, my stomach was still twisted into a knot. Though a dream revealed my first step, the endeavor to make it a reality seemed far-fetched. The enterprise was like gold in a mine on the edge of a jungle in the Amazon forest … and I had no way to transport it to the city. But I made an inner oath to cross the finish line no matter how treacherous the road might be.

Seeking reassurance for my venture, I met with a power player. A big man with an unshaven face, double chin, and thin curly black hair … he was a scary sight.

For 20 minutes, I attempted a description of the aspiration. "To create a global project with works of art and written stories that will be a cultural intersection. Cross-cultural creations that will be reborn again and again, sparking the imagination of each generation."

The man just looked at me.

For a second I was happy. I had been given the chance to express my aspiration, and it seemed that someone really listened.

"So, let me see if I get it," the man said with a stony voice. "You are in a foreign land. English is not *second nature* to you. You have no family here, nor any money. You never wrote or designed anything. You didn't go to school, and you have no knowledge or experience in the industry."

The man took a sip from his brown beer and blockaded the road. "You have just wasted my time with the worst joke. Do yourself a favor and quit. Even luck won't be able to help such a stupid thing."

A century ago … there was a *transformed* Indian lad named Srinivasa. With no experience or formal training, the lad changed the landscape of mathematics in his 20's.

Professors of the highest ranks were puzzled by how this was possible. Srinivasa was a human being who *united the opposites* from within; he was at once a genius analytical thinker, and a devoutly spiritual man who received esoteric mathematical formulas through dreams.

Each human being can do the impossible … he or she should first *decide* to *free the mind*, so as to see the unreachable star.

The next day, I traveled to a remote mountain. There, I spent 4 days in a cave, meditating on the dream that had expanded my enterprise.

The Ring of The Moment endowed by *The Equation*, focused my mental state.

On papyrus papers I purchased, I began building the innovation: writing the insights and story-lines, and childishly painting basic designs of exotic worlds and space-like elements.

I immersed myself in the moment, for it is the messenger of both the subconscious and the Universe.

The moment is filled with binary codes, which reveal the future's secrets. When the mind is free, one picks them up, just as an antenna listens to sounds from outer space.

When the first phase of the innovation was finished … I returned home to discover a painful surprise.
For years, the lad had sacrificed his youth and the joys of life to free the mind, to work hard, and to break the mental barriers that prevent the heart from experiencing happiness.

Yet this same effort … would become his own *trap*. The *spiritual* phase was over … it was NOW time to go back to reality, the *physical* world, and strive to generate interest in the enterprise. "What is the value of a creation if it sits on the shelf?" the lad pondered.
"The artist and the entrepreneur should strive to make it a reality."

But right there … was an age-old problem.
In certain industries, many buyers think in terms of stock characters, logical models that make sense to *The Intellect System*.

When the lad came to speak about his innovation, things just made no logical sense to the buyer. And because the buyers were chasing *time* … opportunity after opportunity perished.

When the lad said he was 22, people would begin to question him, thinking that he was a man in his 30's.

"Who created all this work?" the wealthy buyer would ask. "I did," the lad would reply.

And at that very moment, nobody would believe him, for a simple reason:

When the intellect thinks about a good artist, or an inventor, or a thinking scientist … automatically it receives an image of a shy, introverted man with glasses and a beard, who is dressed in simple grey clothes, and by nature is not a speaker or doer. And when the lad did not fit this logical model … a rifle fired at his dream.

Dear Mother

It seems like I have reached a dead end.
I believe the Universe always conspires to lift
those who fight for their aspirations … but I fear
I was skipped.
I am so thirsty for an opportunity … but if this continues,
I will seriously consider inventing waters that restore
people's youth … just so that a single door might open.

One day, as a bright, peach horizon and deep, blue skies bathed the earth, I was sitting, leaning against the trunk of a tree.

My hands were playing with soil samples … when a gentle wind caressed my cheeks, lifting my eyes to see a web of gnarled branches swaying high above my head.

Then, in the skies … a band of birds flew by, creating the shape of an arrow. I seized the moment and ran after them.

After many minutes, I was panting at their stopping point: a building with a golden dome. The birds circled the dome and soared away. "What is this omen trying to tell me?" I wondered.

Quick research revealed that the city had a new mayor, and the building was his workstation.

I sent him a letter, and to my great surprise, he invited me as a guest. His name was Jimmy, a man of vibrant moral fiber who decided to give me an opportunity.

Dear Mother

A big battle was fought, Mother. Weeks of walking
in the soaking rain to explain my innovation have worn
on me a little.

164

But the Universe marshaled some support; the mayor
who governs a city in the hills bound his signature
to a contract that shall progress my enterprise.
Look, Mother ... I am following the lighthouse and
fighting to reach my star.
With Love
James

Jimmy and I endeavored together for the enterprise. Traveling to distant places to meet people of importance, we followed in the footsteps of other people, whose visions were memorialized in the museum of success.

Although ears were now more attentive because of the mayor's name and influence, difficulties still led the lad to walk circles.

"What can I do?" I wondered. "While I can devote my life to my dream, the mayor has other responsibilities. Every human aspiration relies on a *decision*, the *self-reliance* of reshaping one's future."

Unlikely Angels.
While one walks down the path, the best exercise for the heart ... is reaching down and lifting people up.

Every person, poor or rich, should always honor those rare individuals who dispensed care in times of despair.

Life is not a sprint, but a marathon. And every time I fell down ... strangers would come by and carry me closer to the finish line.

At times when I was hungry, a home would invite me for a hot meal. At times when I was on the brink of poverty, a wealthy man would give me some coins. At times when I longed for a human touch, a poor maid would kiss me on the forehead. At times when I was sick, a doctor would treat me, saying, "May you be blessed, boy. Go in peace."

And though all angels are equal ... no angel stood higher than the broadcaster of Olympus.

Mr. King

One cold night, a fire crackled in the fireplace of a restaurant. An air of antiquity permeated the place. Suddenly the screen in the restaurant flickered to life.

There I saw a man with large silver-rimmed glasses, suspenders, and a deep voice.

165

The moment I saw this famous figure, a flame shone on my horizon, guiding my way … when suddenly my old friend, a long time supporter, surprised me from behind, "Still drinking only water, kid?"

"Bloody hell …" I said. "Charles … you scared me."

"Can I sit?" he asked, shooting me a smile.

"Certainly," I replied. "What are you doing here anyway?"

"Came to play with some forks and corks. Hey, may I have a glass of Champagne here?" Charles attracted the server's attention. "Tell me, what's got you so transfixed? You looked bewitched there for a second."

"No, nothing. I just got this magical feeling when I saw this man." I pointed to the restaurant's screen.

"Who, Larry?" Charles asked.

"Yeah, I think that's the man's name."

"Well blemish my reputation acting like a monkey!" Charles was stunned.

"Where do you live, under a rock?!"

"Alright, I'm sorry," I said. "It's not like the man is your friend."

"Actually in 2 days, I am having a gala," Charles said. "And give a guess who will be there …"

My eyes brightened with sincerity. "Charles, may I come? Don't be angry, an eye for an eye ends up making the world blind."

"Kid," Charles said, "Just don't come in that wrecked car of yours."

My spirit unrolled a flying magic carpet … and soared to the skies. The hall seemed like a grand ball-room, crowned by a chandelier.

People were leisurely moving about, music was playing, and food was being served … all made me timid, though my friend Jimmy was with me.

People who conveyed power approached Mr. King, while I, but a poor young man with a dream, slipped shyly into a corner.

Then, as Jimmy was approaching him, Mr. King caught sight of me. He smiled in a *mystical* wise way, as if he already knew what my heart longed for.

"What is your name, young man?" Mr. King asked.

"My name is James, sir," I swallowed. "James …"

"What is it that you have?" Mr. King said.

"A dream, sir."

166

"Do you have any family here, James?" Mr. King asked.

"No, sir. I don't."

Time slowed down … and the man's eyes turned teary. "Here …" Mr. King handed me a handwritten note. "A long time ago someone lifted me up … maybe it's time to return the favor."

On my way back home that night, I saw a man on the street trying to sell his meager provisions.

The man squinted his eyes in hopes of making some coins, and I greeted him and inquired about his items.

Then, I saw a little old book. I opened it, and the pages told a small story … *Every year, in an unknown day and an unknown place, The Source of Light calls upon 4 human beings from 4 different corners of the world. "Bless me," The Source of Light says. "We …" the humans tremble. "How can we bless YOU? We are nothing but dust."*

"Bless Me," The Source of Light entreats.

Taken aback by the force of The Source, they start to stammer.

*"**BLESS ME!**" The Source thunders.*

Suddenly, East and West are as one, North and South are as one, and the people pray transcendently … "May you, The Source of Light, have the power and the compassion to bestow upon us the wisdom to see that we are the creators of our own destiny."

*A **Tear of Light** falls from the skies, and The Source echoes …*

"Amen."

The story reminded me that the Universe transforms the lives of those who **transform** themselves.

And 4 days later, I took up *The 4 Rings* of *The Equation*, embracing the belief in the infinite reach of the mind and the heart.

There were numbers on the note Mr. King had given me … but numbers can lead to intellect, and intellect can confine the mind, caging courage.

So I decided to drive to his home.

"Who are you?" a Latin lady asked.

"My name is James, ma'am. I am here to see Larry."

"Do you have an appointment with, Mr. King?"

"No, ma'am. But I believe he knows me," I said.

"I beg your pardon?" The lady was startled.

"Ma'am, don't cast me away … 5 minutes will be sufficient."

She saw that the young man in front of her just had a will to fulfill *a dream*.

"But Mr. King is not present at the moment," she added with a softer voice.

"Well … may I wait for him here?"

The lady smiled lightly. "No … come on in. It is cold out there."

An astounding house revealed rooms linked together by a circular hall way. "Wait here," the lady said. "I expect Mr. King to arrive shortly."

I entered a trophy room with a spectacular display of golden medals, rare artifacts, and elite awards.

Suddenly, the door of the entrance was open. I peeked, and saw Larry moving forward like a force of nature.

When he saw me coming out of the trophy room … his eyes grew wide as if he was seeing a ghost. "Wait for me there," he said with a serious voice.

Several minutes later, he came back.

"You must be angry," I said.

The man just stared at me, and a smile of pure care spread across his face.

"Not today, kid … Not today. I like this audacity of yours."

For 10 minutes, I dared to describe my dream, my innovation. Afterwards, I said to him, "Larry, I believe we can do extraordinary things together … I promise I won't let you down."

Larry closed his eyes for a split second as if he sought to connect to the strata of his soul, and then said tenderly, "Very well then. Off you go. You'll need some rest."

"For what?" I asked.

"Your training."

Dear Mother
> *You raised me up on your shoulders so I'd see farther.*
> *You raised me up so I'd cross oceans.*
> *19 months ago I was but a poor immigrant, and now*
> *one of the most powerful people in the world became*
> *not just my partner and a mentor, but a Guardian Angel.*
> *My dream has entered a shuttle to the farthest star in*
> **The Galaxy.**

Love You Forever.

168

CHAPTER 37
The Galaxy of Gods

One day, after turning left on Avenue of the Stars, I saw a street that was very familiar. Its heroic name was; The Galaxy. So I decided to name my dream, my innovation, *The Galaxy of Gods*.

When I told Larry the name, he said, "Not too impulsive, not too cautious. I like it. Very much like the relationship between the Titanic and the iceberg."

"What do you mean?" I asked.

"No matter how big the dream, always be aware of the unseen."

Larry's voice seemed to travel from the edge of the galaxy. Each lesson was bathed with wisdom and broke the bonds of earthly confinement.

Larry was a master of *The Moment*. "Magic and miracles transpire when you let go," Larry said. "That does not mean you should not strive. *Strive*! But let life also guide you as you go by."

As I watched him, I witnessed how the mind can unite opposites. To *transform*, one *decides* to shed *a tear*, to express the inner pain. Yet Larry was like a rock that no *tragic* wave could break. So how can one transform if nothing affects the mind?

That's the beauty. One accepts the *pain* seamlessly … and each transformation strengthens one's mental state to a higher level … until all opposing powers live together in the mind for mutual advantage.

"Flowers have been producing *thorns* for thousands of years," Larry said. "Endure them. They are the challenges before the championship."

"Wow," I thought as Larry spoke. "What a miraculous climate humans create when they judge strangers by the content of their dreams and ideals. Here I am, a young man with no status or experience, holding a ticket, an opportunity, gifted by a renowned man who has achieved great success. Larry purely wants to see me happy. And no matter how draining the enthusiasm of the pupil might be … the mentor just sparks a smile."

"Are you listening to me?" Larry startled me out of my wandering thoughts. "Know how to listen," Larry pressed on. "You will not just learn more … but also defend the freedom of expression."

"Larry, can I ask you something?"

"Ask, kid."

"If one has a dream, and walks a path, and it leads to nowhere, should one stay on the same road?"

"The entrepreneur ponders this too, 'If I have a plan and it does not work, should I change it?' Kid …" Larry said. "If it's not broken, don't fix it. First, feel if you're *following your bliss*, if the dream is what the heart longs for. Then, if the road seems to be a dead end, don't hasten to jump from one road to another. Let it integrate with the times. The right road is often the one with the toughest tests."

Time turned, and the training continued. "You speak too much," Larry said. "Remember, life and death are in the tongue. See the words before you say them. Let every sentence be the bottom line, a sense of essence. You will need it …"

As a part of the training, Larry sent me to seek the advice of some of the world's most successful people. "When you share your convictions about *The Galaxy of Gods*," Larry said, "Remember, though you're looking at tigers, don't avert your eyes from theirs. If they sense fear, they will bite. But if they see fierce belief, they will listen."

Several months had gone by, and I was ready for my first task, a round in the fight for my dream.

There was a man named Jona, a wealthy man who had survived the *Global Tragedy* that swept Europe in the 20th century. Infinitely fair-minded, yet tough, he was on his way to check if my convictions could convince him.

As my vehicle traveled forward, I felt as though something was missing. Searching … I saw that I had forgotten my tie.

Morning had just broken, all the stores were closed, and minutes away was a place to which I couldn't be late.

Then, suddenly, I saw a man crossing the street. A young girl was walking behind him and picked up the wallet that fell from his pocket. She returned it to its rightful owner, and I shouted, "The Ripple Effect!"

I approached the man and said, "Excuse me, sir, there is an important place around the bend I can't be late to. I forgot my tie, and all the stores are closed. May I have yours?"

170

"You want me to give you my tie?!" the man exclaimed in surprise.
"Yes, sir. I will pay you for it."
Pausing for a second, the man retrieved a memory and recalled the girl who *stood up* for what was right. Passing it on, he took off his tie and said,
"Here ... take it. I wish you success."

When I arrived at the place, Larry smiled as though triumphant trumpets were playing a fanfare, and together we welcomed Jona. As I started to stretch the extent of my convictions, Larry signaled me to be in the moment and speak from the heart. So I closed my eyes, called *The Rings* of *The Equation*, and said, "Jona, 73 seconds after liftoff ... a shuttle exploded into a ball of flames. 7 people died. That evening a young prince canceled the State of the Union so as to pay tribute to the nation's pain. You see, the tragedy of the shuttle, as with the global tragedy you survived, transformed lives to march in unison and touch the stars. Jona, you lost your dearest ones in the fires, but you decided, in spite of, and against all the risks, to fight for your future. I hope you can see that all I desire is to fulfill my dream."

Jona stood up, looked at Larry, and then said to me, "I don't want anything in return. I will give you what you want, and speak with my friends to do the same."

∞

When Benjamin Franklin was asked, "Well Doctor, what have we got ... a Republic or a Monarchy?" Mr. Franklin replied, "*A Republic ... if **YOU** can keep it.*"

Always climb the mountain, and though the Universe strengthens your spine, let every achievement still find you on the front-line.

The innovation was nourished with the coins and bills necessary to evolve it. Now, with the seas calmer, the fight for the dream gathered speed towards the lighthouse.

When the lad had traveled to the cave, the place where he finished the first phase of the innovation – writing the insights and storylines, drawing the elements he saw in his dream – he had exercised his self-reliance. An entrepreneur should not sit on the sidelines expecting others to take the initiative he or she fears.
Yet profits and prosperities have a propensity for making one stand

idle. The lad's creations were but a fraction of the road, and the finish line did not yet shine on the horizon.

When he again lifted a lamp to light the land of the innovation … he did not grasp how to transport it from his mind to reality. So the lad approached writers and artists he had met on his path.

21 writers and 12 artists brushed aside his innovation speculating that it would take 5 years just to build the foundations.

After Larry had gathered a group that represented 2 of the most famous artists in the world, and they chose not to help, it would be fair to say that the lad was crushed.

"James," Larry said, "Through the hurdles of the night we will make it together. Be strong. See your guiding star in the skies."

A Code's Road

When a tragedy strikes … a tear transforms.
When transformation is accomplished … the opposites are united.
When the opposites are united … the mind is enlightened.
When the mind is enlightened … destiny is designed for the light.
When destiny is designed for the light … the network of energy is influenced.
When the network of energy is influenced … bad decisions are corrected.
When bad decisions are corrected … living things are purified.
When living things are purified … perpetual peace sweeps.
When perpetual peace sweeps … lofty heights descend onto Earth.

Though without experience, I decided to climb the mountain and finish the innovation by myself, first crafting the 2 manuscripts from my dream.

Not long ago, there was a well known man named Mr. Cayce. A man with super powers, a modern Nostradamus, he predicted events before they transpired and cured thousands of people from illnesses.

He accessed the subconscious of the human in front of him, and *picked up* the answers.

Mr. Cayce loved all human beings as they were, and he did not believe in talent. For when the mind is *free, anyone* can accomplish what he had done.

As I crafted *The Galaxy of Gods*, I came to believe that when the mind is transformed, the Universe looks at itself through one's eyes. The mind becomes a microcosm of the Universe, and all its secret knowledge becomes a magical library in one's own mind.

For the next 4 months, I would wake up at the break of the dawn and *decide* to sacrifice efficiently.

An Avatar is the higher self, the super character one creates after transformation frees the mind.

To reach my Avatar, I would blind my eyes with thin tape and black glasses every morning and wander the streets with a cane. For when the eyes are closed to earthly things, a third eye is opened to wonders of infinity.

Old people and children would assist me in crossing the streets, and when my eyes shed *tears*, I thanked them. I could sense life as if through screens of energy.

Back to the basement where I based my work, I started to spill the words of the 2 manuscripts. On the table lay an astrolabe … and with *The Equation*, I wore opposite hats. I donned the hats of the poet and the painter; the poet perceives the emotions, and the painter, the spectrum of colors. Then came the hats of the scientist and the engineer; the scientist puts on paper what the engineer applies in practice.

Time moved in slow motion as I dove deep into the subconscious. The subconscious is the grand gallery of the mind, a hall of records that dates back to the beginning of time.

As I crafted the 2 manuscripts of the innovation, I picked up a note from the subconscious.

Measurements in Roman units and royal feet revealed the nexus between the buildings of today and the structures of the past. Some share the same dimensions, the same geometrical coordinates.

So I meditated on the numbers 144, 50, 30, 60 and applied them to the structure of *The Galaxy of Gods*, like glass that is melted and then returned to its original state, but in a new form.

As the ink of my pen spilled the words of the 2 manuscripts … I was given a choice: to direct the innovation to be a force of good or ill?

As an inspiring prince once said, "For space science … Whether it will become a force of good or ill *depends* on man."

The creator of any innovation is faced with the same choice. The world's consciousness is the house of both good and ill decisions made by human beings since the dawn of history. So an ill decision made 10,000 years ago, still impacts decisions today, for energies are interconnected.

Ill decisions are those tempting energies that entice the mind to repeat the same mistakes of the past. They appear to be challenging, and they promise fame, which camouflages a fall.

The more transformations enlighten the mind, the more one is immune to these enticing energies ... for in the light, they fade away.

When the last word of the 2 manuscripts was written, I felt as though I was flying in the sky on a balloon filled with helium.

But suddenly, a shock rippled the times. The collapse of the Bronze Bull was like a sonic weapon sounding a *global tragedy*.

Its crash resonated in the streets of the world, steepening the slope of an already uphill path. Discord and fears deferred the dreams of many, but I believed I could not turn back. I would climb the mountain and fight to cross the finish line.

The tragedy reminded me that, while we come from different places and speak in different tongues ... our dreams beat as one.

And it was there that courage was discovered. I met a painter named RV, a young man who aspired to become the breadwinner of his little family by means of creating art.

I shared with him the elements I saw in my dream ... and though I had only a few coins in my pocket, the young man sacrificed everything so that a stranger could fight for his dream and cross the finish line.

Together, RV and I, created all the works of art I had seen in my dream: the superheroes, the cards, the costumes, and the worlds in space.

Nights would find me on the hills, under the sparkling stars, working on *The Galaxy of Gods*.

I would try drawing those magical elements I had seen in my dream for RV ... their shapes and vividness of color.

I would look at the stars. Though far, far away, they appear like little children ... they are grand celestial bodies that whisper, "What causes change to move time?" And entrepreneurs reply ... "Innovation."

On the third anniversary of *The Galaxy of Gods*, my heart burst into light when RV presented all the elements of my dream.

174

I seized *the moment* and drove to the house of my Guardian Angel. I stood outside the gate. Holding the 2 manuscripts and the artwork, I held my right arm high, waving a flag with the symbol of *The Galaxy of Gods*.

I then stormed into Mr. King's home.

Passing perplexed stares, I reached the parlor. There, with fervor, I started to raise the flag atop a golden base.

As the windows were flooded with the inspiring light of the day; Larry put his hand on my shoulder and said, "I am proud of you, kid. You have come a long way …"

"Hello." I answered.

"James, it's Larry. Listen, in 4 days you'll get a shot at the title. One of the biggest conglomerates in the world will challenge your innovation."

"Will many people be there?" I asked in fear.

"A fair few. The president and his governors."

"Will I see you?" I asked.

"Yes, I'll be there."

"Thank you, Larry. I love you."

"… I love you too, kid. This is your fight to fulfill your dream."

As a fighter wears his belt, I put the symbol of *The Galaxy of Gods* on my lapel, and drove in the direction of a new dawn.

As my old car crossed a canyon, smoke suddenly swirled from the hood, fluctuating a needle furiously.

I pulled over, and the frenzy on the freeway left me all alone. I peered up to the crest of the mountain above. I kneeled and prayed … "The Source of Light, let me get up from my knees. Not because of strength or mind … *but because of spirit* …"

"Hi!" a voice pierced through the air.

I shifted my sight, and saw a silver-haired man standing there.

"Are you all right?" the man asked, raising his voice.

I stood up and said, "Yeah, I was on my way ahead, when this trouble obstructed my path."

"That's all right," the man said. "I *believe* I can help you."

As the man put his best foot forward to aid me, his 2 daughters ran

175

out of the car to say hello. "Do you know our father is a firefighter?" said one. Then the other girl said modestly, "He always says to us, 'The love of a single heart can save lives.'"

Soothing the strain, the man watered the turbulent part of the car, and said,

"You are set to go."

The finish line began to shine on the horizon as I entered the ring.

The conglomeration was a place I had never seen before. It seemed like a city with rules dating back to medieval times. Gates, long black cars, guards patrolling the perimeter … all made it seem as if spears might spring out of thin air.

In a gargantuan hall, I saw the back of my great mentor. He turned to me, and his lips parted in a half smile, "You're late, kid."

"Mr. King, they are ready," the clerk came to declare.

"Don't be afraid," Larry whispered. "I believe in you."

Together we moved forward through a corridor on a higher floor, where a heavy door was already slightly ajar.

Larry sparked a loving smile, and went ahead of me, as if to shield me should a bullet be shot.

The door opened with a low, drum-like rumble … and the fight began. When the president and his governors leapt to their feet to greet Larry, I feared that if I looked at them I would turn into stone. Waiting tigers, helmeted warriors …it seemed as if fire gave way to ice.

As the fight for my dream accelerated, I slowly felt how the Lords of Wealth were taking me on mentally … and I was bleeding energy. A sharp pain seared across my spirit. Jaw locked, body rigid, stiff as a board … I looked to Larry for help … but he remained silent.

Danger lay before me, as I could not distinguish between the transparent windows and the opaque walls.

Now standing alone in this titanic room, a memory suddenly carried me through time to see my younger self.

Eyes closed, I saw myself in my old home where my roof was shining high and bright like the morning star. I remembered the scars, a solitary childhood, and my mother whispering, 'Good night, my light.' The hearty laugh of my family along with the playing of the piano … all my adventures across the world … this innocent search for purpose … the struggle and the progress that had brought

176

tears, miracles, and loving strangers who sacrificed so that a dream would be fulfilled.

When I returned to the moment, fear vanished, and I fought in the ring, "Gentlemen, good morning. My name is James, and I have the honor of being the creator of *The Galaxy of Gods*. 3 years ago I decided to put forth everything I have to pursue the initiative of creating a simple and inspiring enterprise. Due to its structure ... inevitable challenges will be met head-on while upholding values.

"Today, profits have eroded in many markets and classes; although borders between nations are blurred, creations are less and less cross-cultural.

"Since the beginning of time, the greatest innovations have not only adhered to the synergy of universal subjects, but also moved people to fix their eyes on something greater than themselves.

"This action, gentlemen ... is the engine for a more perfect achievement."

The room's lights dimmed as the screen began displaying all the elements of my little dream.

The music played like a parade. Larry's eyes were teary when the moment reached its climax. Then, when everything faded away ... the fight was over, and the president asked, "Did you do all this work?" I turned my head to the window. Shafts of light inspired me to smile a bit and say, "No ... **LIFE** is the unsung *hero*."

Several days later I was meditating on a remote mountain.

The sand's color was honey, the crisp breeze swayed the bright green leaves, the birds were chirping melodies and though the sun was setting ... it was rising in another part of the world.

Suddenly ... a gust of wind awakened a device next to me. I picked it up and answered ... "Hello ..."

Time Stopped!

A tear fell as a flower falls on the sand ... and is swept away by

nightfall.
I closed my eyes ...
I slowly strove to stand up ...
My legs too weary to take new steps ...
Belief guided... and the eyes awakened to life!

EPILOGUE

If a heart hears these words today ... my moment of loss is your success.

I lost in the ring, but my little dream lives on. A human is but fleeting flesh. A dream endures for eternity. The pains of the loss are the *tears* of a parent who has lost a child, of a human being who has braved the beatings for the shores of the lighthouse.

But I know my dream is happy now, for I was loyal all the way. One infinite garden, yet many trees. One humankind, yet many stories.

It has been 25 years of my life on this beautiful Earth, and I never told this story before.

And because pure pain transforms, I sit now in my home, alone. Outside, Christmas-tree lights illuminate the skies, and your eyes read the words of my life.

The rain is falling down to wash away my tears, so I will see the rainbow. A new journey is at hand, and I shall follow my guiding star, no matter how far.

And if one day you see my little dream out there ... remember to reach for your own. Believe that the future will unfold for you a thriving life.

An age will come when people will passionately compete to fulfill the dreams of others, for we are none but one.

When there are tears ... we shall transform
When there is darkness ... we shall light
When there is hate ... we shall love
And where there is division ... we will unite!